ATTACKING ANXIETY & DEPRESSION

a comprehensive, cognitive behavioral-based solution fostering strength, character and self-empowerment

STEP 1: Before you begin, read through <u>ALL</u> the pages in the workbook up to the section marked Lesson 1 (pg. 1-1)

STEP 2: Follow the schedule listed on page vii for each and every Lesson. Each audio cassette represents one-full-week. This schedule shows you what to do from day 1 all the way through day 7 of your Lesson week.

STEP 3: Once you've completed pgs. 1-7 & 1-8, return to The Midwest Center (optional)

Table of Contents

AS YOU BEGIN YOUR JOURNEY...

Hello! Welcome to The Midwest Center's self-help, home study course for anxiety, depression and related disorders. *ATTACKING ANXIETY & DEPRESSION* represents my life mission. The tools and techniques herein are the same that delivered me from the depths of despair. It is very common to experience some mixed emotions as you begin. Some people feel excited, nervous, even a bit jittery at first. Some are initially skeptical, having tried a host of different therapists, therapies and medications to no avail. Take a moment and remember that this program has evolved over 15-years, it is a STEP-BY-STEP process and it works!

This may be the first time you have ever sought help. This may be your "last resort," as you have tried everything before, maybe spent hundreds, even thousands of dollars over the years on methods that promised recovery or at the very least, relief. You may be saying things like, *"I know it all, I've heard this before, This is more information than I need, I've been anxious too long to ever change, No one is as bad as me, My case is different, It's just too late for me."* Perhaps you remember being told, *"You'll just have to learn to live with your anxiety."* If you are experiencing any of these feelings, try to relax and rest assured that these are just normal negative thoughts. Don't let thoughts like these discourage you before you even begin. Give us a chance - give yourself a chance. In addition, remember we've been here since 1983 - we wouldn't still be here today if this program didn't work. Furthermore, by following the schedule listed on page (vii), you WILL know if this program is worth your investment before your 30-day trial period expires.

The Midwest Center for Stress and Anxiety is a credible, professional organization. We are members of The Anxiety Disorders Association of American, the National Mental Health Association and the BBB of Toledo, Ohio. You may have seen me on *OPRAH* (3-times!), *REGIS & KATHY LEE, LEEZA, THE VIEW With BARBARA WALTERS* and more. We have provided workshops to nationally recognized companies such as: Ford Motor Co., Chrysler Corp., McDonald's, AT&T, Bureau of Workers Compensation and many more.

The skills in this program are so effective and broad based that they would help ANYONE acquire better methods for coping with chronic stress, anxiety and depression. Corporations pay thousands of dollars to have their employees trained in the use of these skills. Individuals going through our group sessions pay anywhere between $1,200 and $1,500 for the same 15-week course you have now. You have purchased one of the most valuable self-help programs available in the world! Give yourself and the program the time, attention and faith deserved. We are very confident that you, like literally tens of thousands of others, will be VERY pleased with the results.

Fondly,

Lucinda Bassett **CEO,**
Midwest Center for Stress & Anxiety

I would be remiss without a special thanks to Carolyn Dickman, Darla Van Horn, and the entire Midwest Center team for their tireless dedication and work. Your efforts are attested in this *AMAZING* 6th revision of the Program! A special thanks also to Judith Nash for her expert editing advice.

SUPPORT SERVICE'S ARE AVAILABLE!

Phone support

The support work that we do is very rewarding. It is our pleasure to help you! We want you to overcome this condition and will do whatever we can to assist you along the path to recovery, including answering your homework, your personal letters and phone support services. If you feel that a call from our support staff will help you with a lesson, a challenge or you just need a pep-talk and reassurance, dial 1-800-515-1133 and schedule the call-back with the person that answers. A support person will call as timely as possible, normally within 15-minutes.

The charge for this service is $1.99 per minute if you wish to be invoiced or only $1.50 per minute if you put the charge on a credit card at the end of the call. Phone support services are available Monday through Friday 9AM to 5PM EST.

If you wish to take advantage of this service, while you are waiting for a call-back, write down what your main need is. What do you need feedback on? Make notes on a piece of paper; that will help keep you focused on the issue at hand. Our job is not to keep you on the line for financial gain. Our purpose in offering this service is to help you as quickly as possible - so it is very helpful if you make some notes before your call-back. When the call comes in, sit close to a clock so that you are totally in control of the call. For over 10-years we had provided phone support services at our expense. When The Midwest Center went national via the television show, the number of people using this service increased tenfold! This greatly increased the volume of calls as well as the support staff. We hired more people and the service needs to pay for itself. However, we are very confident after working with literally thousands of people that the phone support service is without equal in terms of total value!

Paid phone support services also provide you with one hidden benefit: it discourages "chatting." While we'd love to do just that, we learn so much from you and are truly interested in people, otherwise we wouldn't be in this line of work. We work with literally hundreds of people from all over the world (*each week!*) and we could never hire enough people to serve our audience if we spent "chatting" time with everyone. The paid system of support keeps the calls focused and to the point, therefore, we can help LOTS of people along their journey. Another important aspect of paid support: it keeps participants in the Program from becoming dependent on us. A commitment to the program is a dedication to getting ones life back, but NOT in tandem with us. Simply put, it would not be therapeutic for you if we put you in the position of making us your safe person/safe place.

Health care Affiliate's

Included with your Program is The Midwest Center Affiliate's List. This is a listing of all health care professionals who want to offer their services to home-study participants who reside in their area. Contact a professional in your area if you feel you need help beyond the scope of this course.

Before You Begin

(Read through ALL pages in the workbook up to section marked Lesson 1 before completing this section)
Please complete the <u>ATTITUDE INVENTORY</u>© below **before** you begin the *ATTACKING ANXIETY & DEPRESSION* program. Completing this evaluation honestly and accurately will help you determine your optimum starting point in the course, ensure you are getting the *level* of help you need and that your time and efforts are maximized. Your answers to these questions represent a large portion of your overall stress level. Complete the questionnaire and compute your score to measure your reaction to internal and external stressors then follow the instructions listed in your overall score results.

<u>ATTITUDE INVENTORY</u>©:   An Evaluation Designed to Measure Your Response
to Internal and External Stress.

     Do you have realistic expectations of yourself and others?
     Are you a perfectionist?
     Are you a victim, play the blame game?
     Do you feel guilty when you have to say "no"?

It has been said that: *"Attitude is everything!"* When reflecting on why we feel stressed and anxious, most of us look outside. We look at other people, institutions, work places and family for the reasons for our distress. The following evaluation will give you an opportunity for insight into the role your basic thinking plays in your level of anxiety.

As you read each statement, consider it not on an intellectual level, but by your emotional and physical response when you make that statement. For example: Number 9, "I must not fail!" Intellectually you may know that we all "fail" and this is a part of life. But when you make the judgement that you failed, how does your stomach feel? Do you go over this "failure" again and again? For weeks, months, years? How does your head feel? What is your tension level? Reflecting in this manner, circle a one, two, three or four. Respond quickly, do not analyze! Your first response is usually the most accurate.

Step 1: Go through the statements at this time; circle the number that best describes your response.

     1 = I never feel this way   3 = I frequently feel this way
     2 = I occasionally feel this way   4 = I almost always feel this way

1. I like to be in control at all times 1   2   3   4
2. I like things to be fair 1   2   3   4
3. I have a hard time saying "no"
 without feeling guilty 1   2   3   4
4. I like things to be perfect 1   2   3   4
5. I have high expectations of myself 1   2   3   4
6. I worry about what other people think 1   2   3   4
7. If I want something done right, I feel
 I should do it myself 1   2   3   4

8. I feel guilty easily 1 2 3 4
9. I do not like to fail 1 2 3 4
10. I feel people should listen better 1 2 3 4
11. I don't like to cause conflict 1 2 3 4
12. People don't appreciate all that I do 1 2 3 4
13. I'm not where I want to be in life 1 2 3 4
14. There is not enough time in my day 1 2 3 4
15. I don't really feel rested 1 2 3 4

Subtotal   __ __ __ __

Total of all Subtotals   _____

Step 2: **Find the subtotal for each column by adding the numbers in each column. (If you circle three number 3's, your subtotal would be 9)**

Step 3: **Add the subtotals together and note your grand total. Consult the score sheet to determine your level of affectedness.**

SCORING

This self-evaluation inventory may help you see that it is your attitude, inner beliefs, your picture of how life *should be*, that is causing most of your anxiety. It is impossible for things to always "be fair." You may have known this intellectually, but this evaluation measures your response and therefore, stress level, when you mentally stomp your feet and say, "*It's not fair! I am a good person. I follow all the rules. I don't deserve this!*"

0-15 **You are a very realistic person. You realize how ridiculous all of these statements really are. Begin *ATTACKING ANXIETY & DEPRESSION* with Lesson 3, Lessons 1 and 2 will not be necessary.**

16-25 **Your attitude is responsible for a mild amount of anxiety in your life. With some minor adjustments, you can improve your stress level considerably. You will want to begin *ATTACKING ANXIETY & DEPRESSION* with Lesson 3. However, if you have ever experienced physical symptoms from your anxiety, you'll want to begin with Lesson 2. Understand that some of the examples from agoraphobics you will hear on Lesson 2 will seem more severe than your experience. THAT'S OK! Be sure and follow the schedule listed on page (vii) for each of your weekly Lessons.**

26-35 **You experience a moderate to high amount of anxiety as a direct result of your thoughts and expectations. You will be less anxious and more content if you learn how to change the way you think. Begin *ATTACKING ANXIETY & DEPRESSION* with Lesson 1 but understand that some of the examples you will hear from agoraphobics on this first Lesson may seem more severe than your experience. THAT'S OK! Follow the schedule on page (vii) for each Lesson tape.**

36-60 **You are probably anxious and dissatisfied with yourself and others much of the time. It is your attitude and subsequent reaction process. You can be taught to see life experiences in a different way. You'll want to begin with Lesson 1 and be sure you follow the suggested weekly schedule for each Lesson on page (vii).**

Most of the statements on this inventory are ridiculous, perfectionist, anxiety producing statements. If you are trying to live with these statements and beliefs, you are asking for anxiety and stress. You can be taught to let go of this type of thinking.

This evaluation also highlights four thinking themes:

~If you circled a 3 or 4 on statements 1,4,5,7 and 9, you may be a perfectionist.

Think about the anxiety it produces to always want perfection when in reality there is no "perfect." We constantly live in the "never arrive" state. When you think that in order for something to be done correctly you'd better do it yourself, two things happen. You end up doing all the work and those you were unable to delegate to also feel disempowered, untrustworthy and inadequate. You'll want to pay special attention to Lessons 3, 4, 6, 7, 8, 9 and 13.

~If you circled a 3 or 4 on statements 3,6,8,10,11,12, and 14, you need to work on being more assertive.

You can learn how to stand **up** for yourself without standing **on** someone else, to love and respect yourself. *ATTACKING ANXIETY & DEPRESSION* will teach you how to be heard without shouting. Are you tired of being a people pleaser, worrying more about what others think of you instead of what really matters, *what you* think of yourself? You'll want to pay special attention to Lessons 3, 4, 6, 7, 9, 12 and 13.

~If you circled a 3 or 4 on statements 2,5,7,9, and 10, you have unrealistic expectations.

This makes you very hard to live with, but the person that you are hardest on is YOU. We are not suggesting that you should have low expectations, rather reasonable, realistic ones. You can learn how to reexamine your shoulds, coulds and expectations. Pay special attention to Lessons 3, 4, 8, 9 and 12.

~If you circled a 3 or 4 on statements 2,8,10,12,13, and 15, you feel victimized and probably spend a lot of time looking outside yourself for the reasons.

You can learn how to: take control of your life, stop being a victim, stop blaming and think in healthy, productive ways. You can *choose* to be happy and peaceful. You are capable of learning how to take charge of your life. You'll want to pay special attention to Lesson's 2, 3, 6, 9, 10 and 14.

It is impossible to "be in control" at all times. Things are not always fair, however, people only take advantage of you when you let them. You can learn to be comfortable with the preceding statements. If you scored high on this inventory, you really need to change the way you think in order to minimize and eliminate some of your distress and anxiety. *ATTACKING ANXIETY & DEPRESSION* will teach you how to think and behave in a realistic, calm and healthy way. We are not born with coping skills and life management techniques-we must learn them. If stress and anxiety are disrupting your life, **now** is the time to pick up the skills that you have not learned yet.

STOP! THIS IS YOUR WEEKLY SCHEDULE

"What is the most beneficial way to use the ATTACKING ANXIETY & DEPRESSION course?" **The following schedule should be followed for *EACH* LESSON TAPE!***

Day 1 of your week: Listen to your lesson tape once. When you walk away from this tape, your mind should be in the "observer mode." Be conscious of your inner dialogue and outward behavior with regard to this week's objective. *"How am I thinking and behaving with this week's subject in mind?"* Observe how you feel when you speak to yourself. Do you feel good, bad, excited, proud or uplifted? Being a mental observer requires nothing more than observing your inner self-talk, reflecting on how you feel and your inner reactions when you speak to yourself. Keeping a written journal is suggested. Lastly, be sure to use your relaxation session, at least once a day as a participant, *three-times* if possible.

Day 2 of your week: Observe again. Be sure you are using your relaxation tape EVERY DAY! It is suggested you use it more than once a day should your schedule permit. Remember to lie down and actually participate in the relaxation session at least once a day. The other times you may use it when you are eating lunch, dressing in the morning- anytime you're not totally occupied mentally. Feel free to use any supplemental materials you may have received with your order, including the Coaching Videos.

Day 3 of your week: Listen to your Lesson tape again, do your relaxation session and read the material in the workbook that corresponds with your lesson.

Day 4 of your week: Be that mental observer again. Do your homework lessons from the workbook. Use any supplemental books, audios or videos you may have received.

Day 5 of your week: Listen to your Lesson tape again. Begin to implement some of the suggested changes in thinking and behaving. For example, in Lesson 1 we suggest that you speak to yourself with the utmost respect. "Catch" yourself using disrespectful tones or words and immediately replace it with respectful language and compassionate tones. Practice/use the new behaviors and skills taught in each lesson.

Day 6 of your week: Continue your observations and practice. Don't forget your relaxation tape, exercise, no stimulants (caffeine, sugar, etc...) and gentle self-care.

Day 7 of your week: Congratulate yourself for being focused, tenacious and dedicated to self-improvement! Today you will want to listen to your Lesson one final time and continue to observe your thoughts and behaviors. Write in your personal journal about your feelings and what you are learning. Even if you are not sure-you ARE ready to begin the next Lesson!

* Depending on your life experience with anxiety, it may NOT be necessary to spend a full week on Lesson 1 of this course. Lesson 1 is an introduction to this course and you may already be familiar with this general information through therapy, reading on your own etc... Begin with Lesson 1 but move on to Lesson 2 if you feel confident you are familiar with the common personality traits, background traits and physical symptomology.

☞ *ATTACKING ANXIETY & DEPRESSION* is all about breaking thinking and reacting habits-that's why this schedule is so important! We are creatures of habit, we don't break habits with knowledge and information alone-*practice* is essential! This schedule affords the structure and repetition necessary for realizing genuine change. You can go **back** to specific Lessons at anytime, but don't jump ahead!

Do you have questions, concerns or need support? Help is just a phone call away! The Midwest Center Support Line is 1-800-515-1133.

Additional Comments & Suggestions

> *Give yourself permission to feel slightly anxious or uncomfortable while initially examining your anxiety and your life.* **This is normal**! *It's never easy to face our fears or hear about the physical symptoms of another. If you are someone who has this tendency, remind yourself that this is an indicator of how powerful your thoughts are. By changing your thoughts, you* <u>can</u> *change how you feel. After completing Lesson 3 of the course, your physical symptoms will not scare you as much. By this time, you'll understand the internal chemical process comprising your response, the dynamic's of your self-talk and have techniques for coping with these symptoms.*

You are about to begin a home study, self-awareness program created to help men, women and even children cope with anxiety and depression. ***ATTACKING ANXIETY & DEPRESSION*** is helping people just like you, from all walks of life, from all over the world. Since 1983, hundreds of thousands of people have participated in programs sponsored by The Midwest Center. No organization has done more to offer hope and help to the millions of people suffering today. From generalized stress, anxiety, panic, agoraphobia and accompanying depression, this program has helped people overcome their fear, worry and debilitating physical symptoms.

As you go through ***ATTACKING ANXIETY & DEPRESSION***, you will develop a more complete understanding of anxiety, what it is and isn't and what it can do both mentally and physically. Many of you will choose to let go of the confined, sometimes negative point of view in which all new information, stimulus and life events are correlated to. You will learn coping skills and techniques that will help you through stressful or normally anxiety producing situations. You will learn to see and respond differently, to be more compassionate with yourself and feel more relaxed and calm.

You will learn to keep your expectations of yourself and others at a realistic level - to live in the precious present moment rather than in some past or imaginable future. You will let go of past regrets and begin to view your "shortcomings" as the *necessary* stepping stones of personal growth. We will teach you how to deal with anticipatory anxiety and panic attacks.

However, keep in mind it takes time to begin to use the skills effectively. Be patient and compassionate with yourself throughout the course! Most importantly, be realistic about your progress-we tend to want results **yesterday**. Remember, you didn't acquire this condition overnight; negative focus of attention and reacting behaviors are *conditioned* over time. It is going to take some effort and practice on your part. But if you do the work it takes, you WILL start feeling and reacting differently. It is an exciting feeling, to suddenly realize you are beginning to internalize a positive attitude and you're looking at life and yourself in a different way.

This program has been developed and refined to meet the specialized experiences and needs of the chronic stress, anxiety and depression sufferer. This program will help those of you suffering from severe anxiety/panic and those who experience a more generalized degree of stress. How is this possible? The same skills and techniques work for both!

THE "DON'T" BOX

- ‣ **Do not alter ANY MEDICATION without consulting your physician!**
- ‣ **Do not skip around**
- ‣ **Do not underestimate the importance of the relaxation session or homework exercises**
- ‣ **Do not try to cram 15-weeks into 30 days, you will only increase your anxiousness!**
- ‣ **If you are not sure you are keeping this program, do your written work on a separate sheet of paper. There is a $40 charge on returned workbooks that are not in reusable condition**

Changing thought and behavior habits involves reinforcement. We have found it extremely beneficial to reinforce various points by repeating them occasionally throughout this program. As you work through your Lessons, you may notice some slight repetition. Be patient, there is reason for it! As you move through the Lesson's ask yourself, *"How does this relate to ME and my personal or professional life? What of the suggestions and techniques can I implement this week? How does this make me feel?"*

Please fill out the Anxiety Evaluation Form on pages 1-7 and 1-8 in Session One and return it to us at Midwest Center, PO BOX 205, Oak Harbor, Oh., 43449. You will find a similar form at the end of the program. Please fill this out and return it after you have completed the Program. We encourage you to write us.

This program is not meant to take the place of professional help for those who feel their situation requires it. Please feel free to use this program in conjunction with your doctor's or therapist's services, it is the perfect supplement to any treatment regimen.

Disclaimer:

This publication is designed to provide information regarding the subject matter covered. The publisher is not engaged in rendering psychological, financial, legal or other professional services. If expert assistance or counseling is needed, the services of a competent professional should be sought.

WARNING: Anyone who experiences depression needs to inform their healthcare provider, be open to the help recommended by that provider and share their thoughts with family and friends.

The purpose of this program is to teach life-management skills in a self-help setting. Depending on the severity of your discomfort and debilitation, you may wish to combine this program with appropriate treatment strategies outlined by your doctor or therapist.

Changing lifelong thinking and behaving habits is not easy, however, we've never had anyone come back and say, *"Gee, I'm sorry I changed."* Find at least one thing to smile about each day, one person to hug and above all - **be kind to yourself.**

The Relaxation Tape

Your relaxation tape is a **very important** element of the *ATTACKING ANXIETY & DEPRESSION* Program. It will help you to become comfortable with relaxing - both mentally and physically. Many of us with anxiety either forgot or never learned how to truly step in to the present moment and just relax. The relaxation tape was designed to help you create and learn to access that peaceful, loving environment within yourself. By using your relaxation tape as directed in the schedule on page (**vii**), you will learn how to get back to the sanctuary within, anytime you need to.

If at first you are somewhat uncomfortable trying to relax with this tape or going through the muscle exercises, don't let that deter you. **It is perfectly normal!** You may have to get used to this method of instructive relaxation. Give yourself time to get comfortable.

By design, you may eventually develop your own relaxation response-a phrase, thought or image that you can use to relax yourself virtually instantaneously, in any situation. It may be a phrase as simple as, *"I am relaxed and calm. I am strong. I feel safe and secure."* You can use this response along with relaxation techniques and positive self dialogue to calm yourself whenever you're feeling anxious, worried or depressed.

There is only one-side to this relaxation tape, but there are two-parts. First we take you through a muscle relaxation exercise. Then we take you through an imagery response. There are NO subliminal contents to this tape!

You should listen to this tape **twice-a-day**, early in the day and before you go to bed if possible. Feel free to listen at other times as well, however, do not use this relaxation session while driving or otherwise operating machinery as it may make you drowsy.

The most important thing to remember about the relaxation tape is we have to be able to calm and relax ourselves. By *practicing* your relaxation exercise in thoughtful, meditative repetition, you will *condition* your mind and body to respond appropriately to your inner voice.

HOW IMPORTANT IS THE RELAXATION TAPE?

By Sande Collins & Carolyn Dickman

(previously published in *THE LESS STRESS PRESS*)

NOTHING, in my opinion, will help speed the process of getting over anxiety disorder more than the relaxation tape, NOTHING. It is that simple and it is right in front of us.

The relaxation tape played on a regular basis can go a long way toward helping you to better manage your anxiety and depression, face your fears, overcome panic and feel better all around. Put simply, an anxious mind cannot exist in a relaxed body.

Please don't neglect this mighty tool. Here are some benefits: learning to identify sets of muscles that are tense, eventually observing that there is one part of your body that seems to be the first site of tension (ultimately you will find that if you relax that part first the rest follow), to set aside time for just YOU, that you are a very important person and worthy of gentle care and kindness.

You will condition yourself in the technique of relaxation and therefore come to associate feelings of relaxation with the tape. At some point in time, as you listen (2-3 times per day for the first 6 weeks) you will be able to call upon the resulting conditioning. For example, let's say you are into the program eight weeks, you're having a challenging day and you say something to yourself like, "*Gosh, I sure wish I felt the way I feel when I am listening to the relaxation tape.*" Your wonderful mind's eye sees the cassette and has the capability of playing back for you, not the tape, but the feelings that you have come to associate with the tape. You can replay your "feelings of relaxation." Another plus is the day that you realize that you not only control what state (happy, angry, etc.) you are in, but can change from a negative state to a positive state.

Other benefits of relaxation practiced regularly include reduction of: major muscle tension, generalized anxiety, irritability, analytical thinking and depressive thoughts. It will help increase: memory, concentration, immune system function, energy level and a sense of control over your moods. But most of all, it will help you put your coping skills from the program into more effective use.

Please be aware however, that the benefits of relaxation are cumulative. It will be gradual over time. It can take up to three weeks or so before you will notice the effects of your efforts. At first it may be hard to find time. It may even be difficult to sit still through the whole tape. The secret - do a little at a time. Maybe at first just do the muscle relaxation once in the morning, then in the afternoon just play the tape while you are doing other things around the house. The next day, or week, listen to the entire tape. What is happening, basically, is it is allowing your body to become more relaxed for longer periods at a time.

LESSON 1

Introduction

"Because people are afraid of fear, they give up acre after acre of their own life."
-Peter McWilliams

Anxiety & Depression: Symptoms, Causes and Common Fears

OBJECTIVES Lesson 1:

‣ To obtain an understanding of the common personality traits shared by people struggling with the challenges of anxiety and depression.

‣ To understand the background experiences that are often found in people with anxiety, stress and depression.

‣ To see that CONTROL is at the base of most of our anxiety.

‣ To begin to identify the positive sides of your personality.

‣ To see that we came to this point through repetition of unhealthy thinking habits and we can change by practicing healthy, positive ones.

‣ To be able to assess your level of depression and dissatisfaction with life and seek appropriate help and guidance when indicated.

‣ To understand that some depressions begin after high stress levels and therefore are alleviated when stress and anxiety are addressed with effective coping skills.

‣ To begin to make some initial changes in the areas you have control of right now. This includes reducing caffeine and sugar, beginning an exercise program and learning to speak to yourself with respect.

Anxiety. A painful uneasiness of mind, usually over an anticipated ill. An abnormal apprehension and fear, often accompanied by physiological signs such as sweating and increased pulse, by doubt about the nature and reality of the threat itself and by self-doubt.

Most everyone will experience feelings of anxiety at some point in their lives. Whether it's the birth of a first child, the loss of a job or in preparation for a major medical procedure, everyone will experience occasions where their stress level will become overwhelming. A close relative of excitement, anxiety can be best described in terms of *worry*, a general troubled or uneasy feeling of apprehension. For the person suffering from an anxiety disorder, the worry is persistent and habitual, often initiated by **unrealistic** situations or thoughts. In addition, this worry is seemingly uncontrollable and often interferes with the ability of the individual to concentrate or otherwise function normally. Anxiety disorders can coexist with other ailments including panic disorder, depression and alcoholism.

It's a condition that has been misunderstood and misdiagnosed for years, affecting one out of every five people. Well over 20-million people.

Some people suffering from anxiety experience pain. Some, do not. Many of their problems are emotional and analytical. They are *learned* habits that can be *unlearned*.

People suffering from chronic anxiety often complain of:

- strong anxiety episodes
- racing heart/chest discomfort
- trembling
- nausea
- hot and cold flashes
- feelings of unreality and disorientation
- dizziness
- scary, uncontrollable thoughts
- depressed feelings
- fatigue
- feelings of helplessness
- panic episodes
- muscle tension
- migraine headaches
- numbness in various parts of the body
- strange aches or pains

Do you have questions, concerns or need support? Help is just a phone call away! Call-a-Coach 1-800-515-1133.

1-2

People suffering from anxiety disorder often have extreme apprehensions about the following:

- dying
- having a heart attack
- fainting
- losing their breath
- going "insane"
- losing control
- embarrassing themselves in front others
- choking
- hurting themselves or someone else

The four most common concerns of the anxious sufferer are:

- dying
- embarrassing themselves in front of others
- going "insane"
- losing control

When a sufferer is experiencing a panic attack, he/she truly feels that he/she will lose control, go "insane" or die if they do not get to a *"safe"* place or person. The *"safe"* place is usually home or somewhere very familiar and comfortable. The *"safe"* person is usually a spouse, child or close friend - someone who can be there if the sufferer needs help.

Believe it or not, there is no *"safe"* place or person.

You are the one scaring yourself, only you can calm yourself down.

This may be very difficult for you to accept right now. That's fine. It's not important that you *agree* with everything from the start.

It is important however, that you listen, participate and believe we do know what we are saying. It has worked for tens of thousands of people before you!

People suffering from chronic anxiety often share similar backgrounds.

Check the ones that apply to you.

- ❏   Alcoholism in the family
- ❏   Strict religious upbringing/family philosophy (control through guilt and fear)
- ❏   Parents with high expectations
- ❏   Siblings parenting other siblings or parents
- ❏   Feelings not easily expressed/displayed
- ❏   Negative emotional environment
- ❏   Lack of praise and approval
- ❏   Nervousness in family
- ❏   Over-reacting family members
- ❏   Feeling that you must always prove yourself as a child
- ❏   Separation or loss of some family member(s)
- ❏   General unstable upbringing with various conflicts

> These, you cannot change

Due to the situation you may have experienced as a child, you have adopted certain personality traits. Listed below are the most common traits found in people suffering from chronic anxiety.

Check the ones that apply to you.

- ❏   Perfectionist
- ❏   Inner nervousness
- ❏   Tendency to over-react much of the time
- ❏   Low self-esteem
- ❏   Guilt ridden
- ❏   Extremely sensitive to criticism
- ❏   Emotionally sensitive
- ❏   Extremely high expectations
- ❏   Inability to make decisions
- ❏   Obsessive thinker
- ❏   Extremely analytical
- ❏   Suggestible to others problems
- ❏   Overly concerned with others opinions of you
- ❏   Tendency to worry about health problems
- ❏   Need to appear in control

> These are things we can *learn* to change

Do you have questions, concerns or need support? Help is just a phone call away! Call-a-Coach 1-800-515-1133.

1-4

Limitations are certain things you cannot do as a result of your anxiety. For example:

- not being able to be alone comfortably

- not being able to drive, alone or with someone

- not being able to go shopping

- not being able to socialize comfortably

- not being able to make decisions

Anything you feel you cannot do or any problem you are having as a result of this condition is a limitation.

List the limitations and/or problems you have that you feel are a direct result of this condition. List them in the order that they concern you.

1. _____

2. _____

3. _____

4. _____

5. _____

6. _____

7. _____

8. _____

9. _____

Example Homework Responses

Earlier in Lesson One, you were asked to check the background and personality traits that applied to you. Most people relate to a background that includes high expectations and overreacting family members.

The personality traits are extremely important. More than likely, you will find that you relate to most of these traits. It is important for you to understand that this personality type and this type of negative, catastrophic, over-reactive thinking is what is *causing* much of your anxiety.

In terms of fears, many people believe they are most afraid of dying, fainting or going insane. Actually, someone who suffers with anxiety disorder very often is afraid of embarrassing himself in front of others.

Common Fears - Examples:

Flying
Socializing
Driving or riding with others
Speaking in front of people
Standing in lines
Being assertive
Taking medications
Traveling
Working
Being in any situation where you are not in control
Eating
Fear of doctors/hospitals
Fear of illness
Shopping
Being alone
Dying
Thunderstorms
Failure
Crowded places
Not being able to get out or leave when desired

Do you have questions, concerns or need support? Help is just a phone call away! Call-a-Coach 1-800-515-1133.

1-6

ANXIETY EVALUATION FORM

Name _____ Today's date _____

Address _____

City _____ State _____ Zip Code _____

Phone _____ Age _____ Invoice # _____

Check the situations and events below that are uncomfortable for you due to your anxiety symptoms. **Using the two-scales below, indicate how often you would avoid the situation or event and how much anxiety you would normally feel in that situation.** If there are particular situations or events that bother you that are not listed, please feel free to add them at the bottom.

Level of avoidance scale	Level of anxiety scale
1 - never avoid	1 - minimum anxiety
2 - sometimes avoid	2 - moderate anxiety
3 - often avoid	3 - extreme anxiety
4 - always avoid	4 - panic feelings

EVENT	LEVEL OF AVOIDANCE	LEVEL OF ANXIETY
Shopping in stores	_____	_____
Eating in restaurants	_____	_____
Eating in front of people	_____	_____
Writing checks	_____	_____
Driving	_____	_____
Traveling distances	_____	_____
Standing in lines	_____	_____
Heights	_____	_____
Bridges	_____	_____
Sitting in meetings	_____	_____
Enclosed areas	_____	_____
Going to church	_____	_____
Socializing with people	_____	_____
Flying	_____	_____
Talking in front of others	_____	_____
Crowded areas	_____	_____
Being alone	_____	_____
Other	_____	_____

Anxiety Evaluation

Check below any of the body symptoms you experience during an anxious period.

○ racing heart/chest discomfort   ○ nausea
○ trembling/nervousness   ○ hot or cold flashes
○ dizziness   ○ muscle tension
○ feeling confused and bewildered   ○ headaches
○ diarrhea   ○ insomnia/sleeping too much
○ shortness of breath   ○ restless feelings
○ numbness in various parts of the body   ○ strange thoughts
○ feelings of fatigue and depression   ○ feelings of helplessness
○ unexplained panicky feelings   ○ uncontrollable bouts of anger

How much do these symptoms bother you? Circle the appropriate answer.

Not much   Moderately   Extremely

Approximately how many times per week do you have panic attacks? _____

List the events, situations and/or opportunities that you have avoided this month in order to block anxiety, panic or feelings of depression:

During a typical day, how much time would you estimate that you spend
     worrying about this problem? _____
Are you on any medication for anxiety or depression? _____
     What kind? _____ **Dosage?** _____
Have you seen a doctor for this problem? _____
     Who? _____ **How long ago?** _____
What bothers you most about this condition? _____

_____

_____

How much does this condition disrupt your life? Circle the appropriate answer.

Not much   Moderately   Extremely

Where did you hear about The Midwest Center? _____
Additional comments about your problem you care to share: _____

_____

_____

_____

_____

Do you have questions, concerns or need support? Help is just a phone call away! Call-a-Coach 1-800-515-1133.

1-8

"I am now the most miserable man living. If what I feel were equally distributed to the whole human family, there would not be one cheerful face on earth." **Abraham Lincoln**

Depression

In some ways it is comforting to know that many great, successful, learned people suffered with depression.

Depression is a condition that can be defined in various ways; its severity ranges from the *"blues"* or a *"bad mood,"* to severe clinical - suicidal depression. A short description of most stages follows:

Moods:

Research seems to support the idea that most "bad moods" are preventable, or at least fairly easy to repair in a relatively short period of time. There will be more information about this in lesson two.

Mild to Moderate Depression:

This form of depression affects approximately eleven million Americans. It can take the form of "the blues" to feeling hopeless. Some diagnosticians are labeling this type of depression, dysthymia (dis-THIGH-mee-uh). (More information regarding dysthymia-in lesson two.)

Clinical Depression:

Depression that is severe, to the point the client loses interest in the outside world, has pronounced and prolonged behavior changes, and at its worse - causes separation from reality. This depression level requires professional treatment.

Suicidal:

The most severe level of depression. The client sees no reason to live and evaluates that everyone would be better off without them. It is very important that you seek professional help.

It is important that you share your feelings with family, friends and physician. It is wise to consult your doctor if you find depression affects normal daily function. It is often reported that depression that lasts more than two months can have biological repercussions and medication may be helpful.

The picture we have of depression is often grossly distorted and therefore, even the mention of its possible presence is enough to frighten us or make us uncomfortable. We have found that a good number of program participants do not realize they are not only stressed and anxious, but also depressed.

Have you ever had the kind of headache that just sits there, not the kind that sends you immediately to find medication, but the kind that is a light irritant? Do you remember how you ignored it, busied yourself and didn't notice it at times? Slight depressions are sometimes handled like that.

So! You think you're weak? *HA!* You are among the strongest people on earth! Look what you have had to do in order to help yourself take control:

1. You saw and acknowledged that there is a problem. This is one of the strongest things you will ever do.

2. You overcame the lethargy, hopelessness and apathy that are so much a part of this condition. This is gigantic.

3. You overcame your fear of the stigma attached to depression. You are a very strong person.

Our goals this week: to identify any depression that may be present, focus on a clear picture of depression and begin activities that will start to alleviate and uplift.

The kind of depression that most often coexists with anxiety is driven by the anxiety. A large number of people who have suffered with anxiety disorders slowly become depressed to one degree or another.

There are two very good reasons for this. Number one, anxiety disorders ARE DEPRESSING! And second, over time the experience of panic, high stress levels, anxiety attacks and lowered self-esteem and self-respect, seems to lead the brain to reduce the amount of serotonin it produces.

The good news is: If the cause of the depression (stress and anxiety) is dealt with and alleviated, the result (depression) should be relieved. If you can remember that anxiety proceeded the depression, you have a good idea as to the cause of the depression.

Do you have questions, concerns or need support? Help is just a phone call away! Call-a-Coach 1-800-515-1133.

1-10

LESSON 1

Introduction

It is important that we be able to evaluate our level of depression and implement the appropriate behavior and coping skills that are helpful. At this time fill out the depression evaluation.

Depression Assessment Scale

Name _____   Date _____

This assessment tool has 16-groups of statements. In each group you are to choose the statement that most accurately describes your present way of thinking or feeling. Read ALL of the statements in each group before making your choice. Please circle only one number per group.

A.   1. I have had no unusual change in appetite.
     2. I have had a mild change in appetite.
     3. I have had a moderate change in appetite.
     4. I have had a severe change in appetite.

B.   1. I am satisfied with my weight.
     2. I am concerned about my weight.
     3. I am not satisfied with my weight.

C.   1. I have had no unusual change in sleep patterns.
     2. I have had a mild change in sleep patterns.
     3. I have had a moderate change in sleep patterns.
     4. I have had a severe change in sleep patterns.

D.   1. I am satisfied with the quality of sleep.
     2. I am concerned about the quality of sleep.
     3. I am not satisfied with the quality of sleep.

E.   1. I have had no unusual change in energy.
     2. I have had a mild change in energy.
     3. I have had a moderate change in energy.
     4. I have had a severe change in energy.

F.   1. I am satisfied with my energy level.
     2. I am concerned about my energy level.
     3. I am not satisfied with my energy level.

G.   1. I have had no unusual change in sexual desire.
     2. I have had a mild change in sexual desire.
     3. I have had a moderate change in sexual desire.
     4. I have had a severe change in sexual desire.

Depression Assessment Scale Cont...

H.   1. I am satisfied with my sexual desire.
       2. I am concerned about my sexual desire.
       3. I am not satisfied with my sexual desire.

I.   1. I have had no unusual change in self-perception.
       2. I have had a mild change in self-perception.
       3. I have had a moderate change in self-perception.
       4. I have had a severe change in self-perception.

J.   1. I am satisfied with my self-perception.
       2. I am concerned with my self-perception.
       3. I am not satisfied with my self-perception.

K.   1. I have had no unusual change in my ability to concentrate.
       2. I have had a mild change in my ability to concentrate.
       3. I have had a moderate change in my ability to concentrate.
       4. I have had a severe change in my ability to concentrate.

L.   1. I am satisfied with my ability to concentrate.
       2. I am concerned with my ability to concentrate.
       3. I am not satisfied with my ability to concentrate.

M.   1. I have had no unusual recurrent thoughts of death or suicide.
       2. I have had a mild amount of thoughts of death or suicide.
       3. I have had a moderate amount of thoughts of death or suicide.
       4. I have had a severe amount of thoughts of death or suicide.

N.   1. I am satisfied with the quality of my life.
       2. I am concerned with the quality of my life.
       3. I am not satisfied with the quality of my life.

O.   1. I have had no unusual change in my health.
       2. I have had a mild change in my health.
       3. I have had a moderate change in my health.
       4. I have had a severe change in my health.

P.   1. I am satisfied with my health.
       2. I am concerned about my health.
       3. I am not satisfied with my health.

Do you have questions, concerns or need support? Help is just a phone call away! Call-a-Coach 1-800-515-1133.

Depression Assessment Scale Cont...

Scoring

Questions A, C, E, G, I, K, M, and O demonstrate either physical or psychological symptoms. Add your score for those questions.

        0-8   absence of depression
        9-16   mild degree of depression
        17-24 moderate degree of depression
        25-32 severe degree of depression

Questions B, D, F, H, J, L, N and P indicate personal satisfaction.

        0-8   optimal personal satisfaction
        9-16   concern about personal satisfaction
        17-24 lacking in personal satisfaction

DO NOT let your score frighten you. If you feel you scored rather high and this concerns you, please talk with your physician about depression. It is common for people suffering with acute anxiety to be depressed. However, if your score is high, you might feel better talking with your physician.

To be repeated during your 11th week, on Lesson 11. Do not look at this first evaluation again, ignore it until you repeat it in Lesson 11. Review and compare your scores after completing Lesson 11.

In each of the Lessons hereafter, you will be given more and more information about stress, anxiety and depression. Recovery is a gradual process and our goal is to help you week-by-week to build a strong foundation of knowledge and skills. Unfortunately, there is no magic switch that turns all the negative feelings off, but there is freedom in awareness. Commit yourself to learning and improving daily, weekly, step-by-step.

Action Assignments

(Action Assignments are NOT required course-work! These assignments are simply constructive exercise. Participate in as many activities as your schedule allows.)

1.   This would be a good week to make an appointment with your doctor for a check up. Be sure that your thyroid is tested. If your depression level is interfering with your daily life, this might be a good time to talk to your doctor about an antidepressant.

2.   In a personal journal, keep track of your anxious episodes:

         a. Where were you?
         b. Time of day?
         c. What did you eat or drink a half hour before the anxiety?
         d. What were you doing?
         e. What were you focusing on (thinking about)?

3.   View Coaching Video number one, **section one.*** (see next page)

4.   Begin to chart a plan to eliminate caffeine, sugar and any other stimulants you are using. Write a clear contract with yourself that details your daily plans for some type of aerobic exercise. Talk with your doctor about this.

5.   Observe your behavior this week. Notice how much your "overdo" personality traits (perfectionism, worrying...) influence your anxiety, stress and depression levels. Catch yourself over doing perfectionism. How does your body feel? What is your emotional state when you realize "perfect" isn't possible?

6.   Develop a "wish list." *If my anxiety and/or depression weren't holding me back, I would....*

         a.
         b.
         c.
         d.
         e.

7.   Toward the end of this first week you may wish to sneak a peek at the end of Session two (2-10) in the workbook. You will find a brief discussion and description of a **breathing technique**. Practice this technique for one full minute, ten times a day. Practice when you are not particularly stressed, anxious or panicky.

8.   Begin reading a motivational book.

Do you have questions, concerns or need support? Help is just a phone call away! Call-a-Coach 1-800-515-1133.

1-14

Good for you! You have just finished one of the hardest sessions. Isn't it always that first step that's the most difficult?

Some people find it hard to hear others' pain and symptoms. That's normal for those of us who are sensitive. Keep in mind the people on the tapes are sharing how it **used** to be. Because of this program they do not live life as they once did. They don't think in the same way anymore. Rejoice with them and know that soon you will be one of the *tens of thousands* who recover.

In each of the proceeding lessons you will be given further information about stress, anxiety and depression. Recovery is a gradual process, our goal is to help you week by week to build a strong foundation of knowledge and skills.

There is no magic switch that turns all the negative feelings off, but there is freedom in awareness. Commit yourself to learning and improving weekly, daily, step by step.

Go out and practice the skills you are learning. You are a great student. You are intelligent, creative and capable. You can change...don't be a victim of your past. You are more than up to taking charge of your life...now that you are learning how.

* The Coaching Videos are a <u>supplemental</u> tool and may or may not be part of your original purchase. Rest assured, if you chose not to order Coaching Videos, you **still** have everything you need in your audiocassette tapes to successfully complete the program.

Do you have questions, concerns or need support? Help is just a phone call away! Call-a-Coach 1-800-515-1133.

1-15

Smile Darn Ya, Smile!

from *LESS STRESS PRESS*

Abe Lincoln said, *"People are about as happy as they decide to be."* I remember a short note in a ***Reader's Digest*** some time ago that has stayed with me. The local pharmacist seemed to be the person the newcomers questioned about the positive or negative points regarding his small hometown. They often asked him if it was a friendly place. He would reply, *"Was the last place you lived friendly?"* If they replied, *"Yes, it was,"* he would say, *"You'll find this is a friendly town."* If, on the other hand, they gave their former place of residence a bad review, he answered, *"Well, you probably won't find this town friendly either. You probably won't like it."*

In general, outside influences have little to do with how happy we are. There are certain inner traits that seem to smooth the path to happiness. People with high self-esteem tend to be happy people. Second, if one feels in control of ones' life, one is much more likely to be contented. Having an optimistic view of life is essential to feeling happy. Positive people draw positives into their lives; the opposite is also true. John Powell (**Will The Real Me Stand Up**), believes that *"happiness is an inside job."*

I have heard it suggested that "acting as if" is a great strategy; I firmly believe this. Research proves that a smile can change our brain chemistry. A smile encourages the production of endorphins, which leads to a feeling of overall well being. We have more control than we realize; we can change our state of mind. Of course, I am not suggesting that we deny our feelings. I am encouraging you to take charge, know your power and not get stuck.

Other research culminates with the powerful fact that laughter is a painkiller. In a study involving patients in unending pain, they found that if the patient laughed for twenty minutes, they were (unmedicated) pain free for two-hours. Another research project proposes that there is a correlation between IQ and our sense of humor. I submit: if you want people to think your smart, you'd better start smiling.

The final trait that seems to be an integral part of the happy person is - love of people. If you find your fellow man interesting and basically enjoy being around others, lead a socially involved life, are outgoing, with a diverse group of friends, you would probably classify yourself as happy.

I recently received the highest compliment I've had in a long time. I have a dear friend, Diana, in Traverse City, MI. I make it a point to travel the 300 miles, exact mileage from my door to hers, for a visit at least twice a year. (That's where the story about Karen and the elevator took place that I mention on the **Driving with Comfort** tape.) The last time I was there she was having a family gathering and since they have always made me a part of their family, I was invited. Before I got there she told her young nephew I would be coming to his house. He hadn't seen me for a time and indicated that he didn't remember me. She described me and where I was from. He brightened and said, *"Oh, the lady who laughs a lot!"* Thank-you, Matthew.

Looking like a genius,

Carolyn Dickman

Education Director

"I am the lock and I am the key."

Six Steps That Will Put an End to Panic Attacks

OBJECTIVES - Lesson 2:

*   Understand how and why a panic attack occurs.

*   Understand that we create the anxiety, the panic and resulting depression with our thoughts.

*   Understand the steps to minimize, if not, prevent panic.

*   Understand that you are your "safe" person and your "safe" place.

*   Further evaluate and understand varying degrees of depression.

*   Begin to practice control and comfort techniques for panic, anxiety, stress and depression.

*   Understand that depression is both physical and psychological.

*   Begin comfort measures for depression.

What causes a panic or anxiety attack?

The answer is really quite obvious.

YOU CAUSE IT.

Nothing outside of you gives you a panic attack. You cause it. Here's how.

After you experience **external** anxiety, you then become concerned with your body feelings and symptoms. You think about them to the point where you actually start to *scare* yourself with them. This creates **internally** generated anxiety.

Your body senses the fear and releases chemical stimulants into your system to strengthen your body so it can *fight or flee* from whatever it is that's causing the fear, whether real or imagined. These chemicals include adrenaline, sodium lactate and cortisol.

As your anxiety level grows, more chemicals are released into your system.

This causes you to enter the second stage of anxiety, the endogenous stage. Now your main concern is no longer the particular problem that brought on the stress. Instead, it's the "weird feelings" and "strange symptoms" that your body is experiencing.

You become so caught up in wondering *"What's wrong with me?"* that you become bewildered and confused. So much so that all your defenses are down, your sensitivity level is up and you go into panic. The anxiety seems overwhelming. You fear you will lose control.

There is one important thing to remember at this time:

You will not lose control, nor will you go insane.

Your mind and body can only maintain this state of anxiety for a few hours at best. Then, you may become extremely fatigued and depressed.

Next we'll talk about external and internal anxiety.

Do you have questions, concerns or need support? Help is just a phone call away! Call-a-Coach 1-800-515-1133.

2-2

External Anxiety

This type of anxiety is generated or caused by something real, something that is going on in your life.

There is a valid reason to feel this type of anxiety.

It could be brought on by something as traumatic as someone trying to physically hurt you. It also could be initiated be something as simple as watching a television show or by your concern about a future event.

Internal Anxiety

This type of anxiety is generated or caused by your concern about your external anxiety and the way it has made you feel.

You only experience internally generated anxiety if you *choose* to.

By choosing to be less affected by external events and externally generated anxiety, you minimize internally generated anxiety.

Life is stressful. Both good and bad situations can cause anxiety. Marriage, low self esteem, career change, having a baby - all of these situations can cause externally generated anxiety.

This stress will bring on body symptoms--racing heart, bewilderment, dizziness and the like. It is normal to feel this way.

What the anxious person does at this time is to add internally generated anxiety that really has no validity. *"What's wrong with me? Am I going to faint? Am I going to lose control and do something stupid?"* These are not valid thoughts because they are not true. There is no reason to worry about these things.

It is the internal anxiety that gets us into trouble. It's from this internally generated anxiety that we get obsessive and carried away - scaring ourselves with untrue thoughts and increasing our body symptoms.

You must learn to stop, give yourself permission to have externally generated anxiety, tell yourself why you're having it and let it pass.

Steps to an Anxiety or Panic Attack and Eventual Exhaustion

> STRESSFUL LIFE EVENT

> Externally generated (justifiable) anxiety

> Chemical releases

> Body symptoms

The next move is up to you!
How will you choose to react and respond?

Wrong Way!

> fear of body symptoms

> internally generated anxiety
> *"Why do I feel this way?"*

> more chemical releases

> more body symptoms

> fear of symptoms worsening

> bewilderment and confusion

> fear of symptoms, bewilderment

> more chemical releases

> **PANIC ATTACK**

> bewilderment, fatigue and depression

Right Way!

> acceptance

> *"What's really bothering me?"*

> compassionate self-talk

> positive distraction

> **CALM**

> **No fatigue or depression**

> **No chronic anxiety**

> **No pain**

Do you have questions, concerns or need support? Help is just a phone call away! Call-a-Coach 1-800-515-1133.

2-4

There is a six-step approach to self-control when dealing with an anxiety attack:

FIRST   <u>Recognize</u> that you are feeling anxious. Accept your body feelings as a symptom of your anxiety and a sign that something is bothering you.

SECOND   Give yourself <u>permission</u> to feel anxious about whatever it is that is bothering you. *"Of course I feel anxious because...and it's okay to have anxiety."*

THIRD   <u>Breathe</u>. First, inhale through your nose slowly for two-seconds, mentally counting one, one-thousand, two, one-thousand. Then exhale through your mouth to mental count of four-seconds - again by one-thousands. Do this for at least 60-seconds.

FOURTH   Use <u>positive dialogue</u> to talk yourself through the anxious time. It WILL pass. Examples of dialogue might be, *"It's just anxiety. It will go away. I will not lose control. I can still go about my business feeling spaced-out. It **won't** hurt me."*

FIFTH   <u>Get busy</u>. Do something to release some of this self-induced stimulation. Your body is like a car in high gear with the brakes on. Don't just sit there! Walk, run, *clean* closets - but *do* something. Distract yourself from the way you are feeling.

SIXTH   Try to see a little humor in the way you feel. You may *feel* weird, you don't *look* weird. Give yourself permission to feel weird for a little while. It's no big deal. Try to figure out what is really bothering you. Is it some type of conflict that you don't want to deal with? Is it a scary thought? Is it a ridiculous expectation you have about yourself? How about the television program you watched last night? What *is* bothering you?

It takes time and lots and lots of practice. But the only way to stop fearing panic and anxiety attacks is to experience them. Then, work your way through them and begin to see that they won't hurt you.

There is no need to run.

You are your safe place and your safe person. You can make yourself feel better.

Please answer these questions about anxiety and panic attacks.

What are you afraid of when having an anxiety or panic attack?

_____

_____

_____

_____

What are some of the symptoms you feel *right before* an anxiety or panic attack?

_____

_____

_____

_____

What symptoms do you experience *while* having an anxiety or panic attack?

_____

_____

_____

_____

What do you *do* when you feel you are going to have an anxiety or panic attack?

_____

_____

_____

_____

Do you have questions, concerns or need support? Help is just a phone call away! Call-a-Coach 1-800-515-1133.

Partner's Guidelines

Things you should do:

1.   Praise often. For even the smallest successes. Your encouragement is extremely important. Praise the participant for even trying.

2.   Encourage his/her independence. Let them "go it alone" whenever and wherever possible, but only if he/she is ready.

3.   Compliment the participant for their progress as far as attitude is concerned. He/she is the last one to notice how they are changing for the positive. Be sure you point it out.

4.   If he/she wants you to go along as they practice his/her avoidance situations - such as driving, shopping etc... - go with them. But allow him/her some distance, all the while letting him/her know you are there to assist and support them.

5.   If you are in a situation where the anxious partner begins to feel panicky and anxious, try to help him/her by reassuring them that it is just anxiety.

     Remind him/her that they are not dying, going crazy or having a heart attack. Reassure him/her that there is no reason to run. There is no safe place. Then distract him/her by showing things to them, using humor or talking about something that they are interested in. Let him/her know that they will be okay, but do not make a big deal out of the fear and panic.

6.   Let your anxious partner have a big hand in the decision-making process - where you are going, how long you will stay and how you will get there and back. Let your partner feel like he/she is in control of the situation to some extent. He/she will be more comfortable and probably will stay longer.

7.   If your anxious partner feels discouraged or depressed about his/her progress, give them reassurance that they are doing well.

8.   STAY POSITIVE

Partner's Guidelines Cont...

Things you should NOT do:

1. Do not make fun of this condition. Never be sarcastic about it.

2. Do not monitor his/her progress by constantly asking how he/she is doing or saying, *"Shouldn't you be doing this or that by now?"* This will only make him/her feel like they are not living up to your expectations. It will make the participant very anxious.

3. Do not tell other people about his/her condition. If your partner wants someone to know about it, it is their right to tell them.

4. Do not baby him/her. Be supportive and compassionate.

5. Do not get angry over his/her fears and attacks. He/she really cannot help it when they feel this way. The longer you treat him/her badly or make them feel guilty, the longer it will last.

6. If he/she is having a panic attack while you are with him/her, do not suggest leaving, going home or to the hospital. Distract them as mentioned earlier.

7. Do not read his/her materials. This program is theirs alone - unless he/she wants to share it with you. Then, by all means, take an interest.

8. Don't be too concerned if he/she seems to change into someone who seems a little angry or selfish at first. That will change. It's just that he/she realizes for the first time that he/she is allowed to be angry and selfish at times and people will still love him/her. He/she will find a happy medium eventually. Praise your partner for being assertive.

Do you have questions, concerns or need support? Help is just a phone call away! Call-a-Coach 1-800-515-1133.

2-8

Example Homework Responses

What are you most afraid of when having a panic attack?
- *embarrassing myself*
- *having a heart attack*
- *getting sick*
- *my legs collapsing/fainting*
- *having to leave work*
- *losing my mind*
- *afraid I am dying of a serious illness*

What symptoms do you feel right before the attack?
- *feeling light-headed, disoriented*
- *feeling out of touch with reality*
- *a need to run*
- *tightness in chest*
- *jelly legs*
- *chest pain*
- *strong physical symptoms*
- *pounding heart*

What symptoms do you feel during a panic episode?
- *sweating*
- *heart palpitations*
- *feelings of confusion*
- *difficulty breathing*
- *feeling that something horrible will happen*
- *acute awareness of body feelings*
- *muscle tension*

What do you do when you feel you are going to have an attack?

POSITIVE - *No more running. Accept it.*
NEGATIVE - *Stop talking, start worrying. How long will it last?*
NEGATIVE - *Find my "safe" place or person.*
POSITIVE - *Distract myself. It WILL go away.*
POSITIVE - *Do something physical.*
NEGATIVE - *Drink or self-medicate.*
POSITIVE - *Use positive dialogue. Find something positive to read.*

When you are beginning the anxiety cycle, it is a signal to you to accept that something is bothering you. Try to pinpoint what it is and then take action to eliminate some of the anxiety by doing and saying positive things.

Homework Responses Cont...

It is important for people who suffer with anxiety disorder to understand that a panic attack is not going to hurt them.

People who suffer with anxiety disorder tend to avoid change, risk and conflict.

As such, when you decide to take chances, to practice some of your avoidance behaviors, you will experience feelings of anxiety. It is necessary to have these physical symptoms *at this time.* They are part of the challenge. Don't let them scare you.

Use positive self-dialogue to understand the positive side of the anxious episode. Of course you feel anxious - you are trying something challenging. It is okay for your heart to pound and for you to feel strange and confused.

Some of you may try to avoid having panic attacks.

Don't.

Instead, let yourself experience these feelings. Use this as a practice opportunity to use your new skills. Learn to view some of these anxious episodes as excitement. Once you are not afraid of the feelings, the anxious episodes WILL begin to dissipate.

BREATHING

When you experience your first sensations of panic, we suggest that you change your breathing right away.

First, inhale through your nose slowly for two-seconds, mentally counting one, one-thousand, two, one-thousand. Then exhale through your mouth to mental count of four-seconds - again by one-thousands. Do this for at least 60-seconds. Next, immediately fill yourself with positive, comforting dialogue. This exercise will help tremendously in preventing a full-blown attack from spiraling.

The mental activity of counting is an extremely effective distraction. The breathing process sends a signal to the brain to relax - things are just fine. The red alert sign is turned off.

Do you have questions, concerns or need support? Help is just a phone call away! Call-a-Coach 1-800-515-1133.

2-10

Using Lesson 2 to help with depression:

As you listen to **Lesson Two** you will find that the main focus is to give coping skills that lead to physical comfort. How do we get comfortable with depression? Honestly? Recovery from depression and anxiety disorders is a process. There is no *"ON"* and *"OFF"* switch. Most physical and psychological changes take time and practice.

Part of getting "comfortable" involves understanding. We must understand that depression is both physical and psychological. If we have been stressed and anxious for a long time (two weeks, two months or two years), the centers in the brain that manufacture the chemicals that keep us in a non-depressed state, slowly become repressed. We are not making enough, for one, serotonin. This is why doctors sometimes recommend an antidepressant. (Remember, an antidepressant doesn't make serotonin--it encourages the brain to do so. This information can be comforting to those who are afraid of medicine.)

This week we would like you to begin taking steps toward feeling better. The six-steps outlined in the program (and on your carry-a-long cards) are to be used not only when you feel the beginnings of panic or high anxiety, but whenever you feel a surge of other emotions as well.

For example: You are in a long line at the store and you begin inner dialogue, *"Why me? Why do I always get in the slowest line? Don't I have enough to contend with?"* As soon as you notice a rise in your metabolism from anger and/or fear, **use** your six steps. Perhaps you come home to an empty house and a wave of down feelings wash over you, *"Nobody loves me. Nobody cares."* Immediately initiate the six steps.

The first three (Notice, Accept, and Breathe 2-4) steps will comfort you physically. The fourth step (changing your dialogue from negative to comforting and soothing) will help you physically AND psychologically.

Every emotion carries its own chemistry. We feel what we think. This is a vital insight whether we are dealing with stress, anxiety or depression. Using the six steps is comforting and shows us that we can change our emotional state and therefore, the associated chemistry.

When we are depressed, motivation is very difficult to muster up. Oprah Winfrey once said, *"Motivation comes with the DOING."* We can only encourage you vigorously to use the aids we have outlined for this week.

Moods: Research seems to support the idea that most "bad moods" are preventable, or at least fairly easy to repair in a relatively short period of time. **Steps:** 1) Trace the mood, if there is something that you can do about the source-DO it; if not, choose your attitude (make it positive). 2) List positives in your life. 3) Exercise. 4) Socialize. 5) Seek humor. 6) Do something nice for someone. 7) Change your environment. 8) Enjoy the arts. 9) Spend time in a natural setting. 10) Speak to yourself as if you were speaking to a beloved friend.

Mild to Moderate Depression: This form of depression affects approximately eleven million Americans. It can take the form of "the blues," to feeling hopeless. Some diagnosticians are labeling this type of depression, dysthymia (dis-THIGH-mee-uh). Use the steps listed above and the coping skills, activities, and cognitive restructuring listed throughout the program. In addition, speak with your doctor, in detail, about your assessment.

Clinical: Depression that is severe, to the point the client loses interest in the outside world, has pronounced and prolonged behavior changes, and, at its worst, causes separation from reality-- needs professional treatment--don't just sit there--TELL someone.

Most of us are frightened of medication. It is possible to recover from depression without medication. However, if the diagnosis is clinical depression, severe depression, if thoughts of suicide are prevalent and comforting, it is time to find out if medication is appropriate for the time being. Talk with your doctor, therapist, pharmacist; get good, reliable information. Often, we are very misinformed about antidepressants.

Depression is like looking through dirty, smudged sunglasses...your view is not clear. Your view is distorted. You aren't seeing things realistically. You are making decisions based on what you see and what you see is not what IS. *"Sometimes the bravest thing we can do is-reach out and ask for help."* YOU DO NOT HAVE TO LIVE THIS WAY.

Suicidal: The ultimate level of depression. The client sees no reason to live and evaluates that everyone would be better off without them. The thought of suicide comforts them. See a physician IMMEDIATELY. Leaving may sound like the only answer...pause just a moment and answer honestly: *"What will this do to the ones I leave behind?"* It is a legacy you do not want to be responsible for.

Reading through this initial information can be anxiety producing. Just because you have some depression does not mean it will get worse. Using our knowledge of cause and effect, if we get at the cause (in most cases: stress, anxiety and the negative ways in which we think), we change the effect. This is great news!

Do you have questions, concerns or need support? Help is just a phone call away! Call-a-Coach 1-800-515-1133.

2-12

Panic and Anxiety Attacks

Assessment: How do you feel? The following statements have been made by very depressed people. **As you think over the last month, which of these statements can you identify with?** If you do not identify with any of the statements you may still be depressed but not as severely. This does not mean you should settle for being a "little" depressed. Using the coping skills outlined in this program will help you to feel better, identify where the "downs" are coming from and make the necessary changes.

- ○ It's hopeless/I'm hopeless.
- ○ I am obsessed with guilt.
- ○ Watch out! I have a short fuse.
- ○ I drag myself through the day.
- ○ I wish I could die.
- ○ I'll never smile again.
- ○ Just let me sleep.
- ○ Everything is dark; I lost my colors.
- ○ I drink alcohol to dull the pain.
- ○ I can't........is my litany.
- ○ I am lonely, even in a crowd.
- ○ I feel like a huge weight is on me.
- ○ I am empty.
- ○ I can't sleep; I wake up after 3 or 4 hours.
- ○ I can't cry-I used to.
- ○ I don't want to see anyone.
- ○ Nothing gives me pleasure.
- ○ I barely function.
- ○ I wouldn't wish this feeling on my worst enemy.

If you have checked more than three of these statements please consult with your physician and begin using the skills in the *ATTACKING ANXIETY & DEPRESSION* program.

Exercise is extremely important for someone with depression. Exercise produces endorphins. This is where the "runners' high" comes from. Going for a brisk walk every day leads to uplifted feelings. Start slow if you have not exercised in a while-gradually increase your speed and distance. Consult your doctor about a reasonable schedule and pace for you.

Partner's Guidelines

Client: *"If one more person tells me to 'just get a grip,' I think I may become violent. Do they think I want to be this way?!"*

Well-meaning friends, family and co-workers, sometimes even therapists, say the most unhelpful things. The intentions are usually wonderful; the messages are often awful.

Client: *"I was brought up to 'pull myself up by my bootstraps.' I swear, at one time I was so far down in those boots - I couldn't see daylight."*

People with mood disorders sometimes need others to point out their symptoms and they may also need someone to literally make the appointment and go with them to their healthcare provider. When we are depressed, our thinking is affected. We see things through smudged, dark glasses. The depressed person blames himself for not taking action which increases his self-loathing and further insures he will not be able to act.

Stigma, unfortunately, still exists when it comes to depressive disorders. We blame it on the flu, the job, the spouse and any number of "acceptable" conditions to have. Literally millions are existing rather than living. Somehow, *if we were stronger* - this *wouldn't* have happened, is too often the thinking. When we are depressed, we have somehow failed miserably at just living.

The significant people in the lives of the depressed person can make all the difference.

Client: *"Bless my friends! They didn't understand panic and agoraphobia, but they sure were scared by the depression. If they hadn't put me in a car and made me go for help, I don't know what would have become of me. It's funny now...they really didn't understand panic and avoidance behaviors like being scared to drive...they made me drive! I would drive to the Midwest Center and they would leave me there, take my car and go shopping!"*

Depression is subtle; it usually builds so gradually that the sufferer may not be aware. *"Something is wrong, but what?"*

At first there may be phantom pains, fatigue, headaches, lots of gastrointestinal problems, muscle soreness, a reported heaviness in the chest or elsewhere. All of these need to be checked out by the physician, but hopefully someone will mention depression along with all the other symptoms.

Do you have questions, concerns or need support? Help is just a phone call away! Call-a-Coach 1-800-515-1133.

2-14

Partner's Guidelines cont...

1. Family and friends need to step in and encourage the depressed person to get treatment. Go with them and wait in the waiting room.

2. Help give the history of the depression if your loved one would like you to. Sometimes an observer can point out things the sufferer wouldn't notice or remember.

3. Be reassuring. *"This is temporary. This is very treatable. You are not weak. You are not a failure."* (Or any other negative self-description.) *"That is the depression talking. Would you be so critical if it were me? Then don't do that to yourself. I love you. Give me the gift of letting me help you."*

4. Get beyond judgement. Your loved one is not doing this for ATTENTION. Depression hurts and it's real.

5. Keep your relationship as normal as possible; this helps provide the feelings of security and stability.

6. It's important to acknowledge their pain but never say, *"I know how you feel,"* unless you truly do. *"I'm so sorry this is happening to you,"* is comforting.

7. Communicating that there is help and that *"You will feel better,"* is vital.

8. Be extra generous with **sincere** compliments and kindness, even if your loved one seems to brush them aside.

9. Treat the depressed person as you've always treated them, with respect.

10. **ADD ANY OTHER HINT THAT WOULD BE HELPFUL IN YOUR PARTICULAR EXPERIENCE:**

If you're feeling depressed, share this page with your doctor, therapist, family, friends....any one that you trust and know cares about you. The depression might say, *"Nobody cares about me."* Following through may be your first step on the road to recovery.

Action Assignments

1. Listen to your lesson tape at least three times this week. Watch section two of volume 1 Coaching Video. Listen to your relaxation tape three times daily.

2. This week we need to begin tapering off caffeine and high sugar foods and drink. You may need two or three weeks to accomplish this. If you are smoking or using alcohol to "calm down," it is time to start charting this and decrease your dependence on these negative behaviors.

3. Initiate the beginnings of a daily exercise routine. Check with your doctor regarding the best beginning for you.

4. Morning meditation. Begin each day: get up fifteen minutes before your household gets busy, sit in a comfortable chair, choose either a spiritual image or an aesthetic one (pink clouds), close your eyes and see the peaceful scene you have chosen. If an intrusive thought occurs simply say calmly, *"Goodbye, it's my time to relax."* Refocus. You may choose a mantra and repeat it over and over. For example, simply the word "peace."

5. Precious, present moment living is a healthy habit. You can stress and depress yourself just lying in bed! This occurs when you habitually mentally "live" in the future or in the past. When you focus all your attention on the here and now, it is difficult to feel either stress or worry.

   Intrusive thoughts can be turned away if you consciously shift your awareness back to the present moment. Practice the next time you are in line, stopped at a light, feel overwhelmed or down. Notice the change in body symptoms as you change back and forth.

6. Move it meditation. As you begin walking, inhale and exhale deeply three times. Set a pace that is brisk but very doable. Begin each step saying, *"One, two, one, two....."* After two minutes, focus outward. Be fully aware of all that you see, hear, smell, feel (you can even taste the salt on your upper lip if you wish). After five minutes go back to, *"One, two, one, two,...."* Keep this pattern, or one you design, for the duration of your walk.

7. Picture peace. Choose several beautiful and detailed postcards or greeting cards. When you feel frazzled or frantic, sit down in a comfortable spot and focus totally on the details in your pictures one-by-one. Try this several times this week; notice how your body feels after just ten minutes.

Do you have questions, concerns or need support? Help is just a phone call away! Call-a-Coach 1-800-515-1133.

2-16

Action Assignments Cont...

8.   Down shift! Do everything this week at a slower pace, walking, speaking and thinking. (If you are feeling blue and sluggish, you may wish to do the opposite.) Make notes in your journal every day regarding this experience.

Choose a symbol or image that reminds you to slow down, a rosebud, or an old cane fishing pole. Put this symbol wherever you spend time: the bathroom (shaving, putting on makeup), rear view mirror, work room or in the corner of your computer screen.

9.   Each day use your personal journal as directed in session one. Make a sincere effort to write down any new insights you have this week and in the weeks to come. Your journal will enable you to see themes, patterns, progress and growth. There is magic in writing.

Write for just five minutes. If you feel you cannot spare the time, maybe we've discovered one of the patterns in both thought and outward behavior that is causing some of your discomfort.

10.   Some individuals report that they have found it to be very therapeutic to write a biography, including their experience with anxiety and depression.

It is equally beneficial to write it again in two weeks, in six weeks, as many times as you feel the need to. Rule: Do **not** reread what you've written. Some find it helpful to destroy what they have written. This seems to symbolize letting go of the past and moving forward into a more peaceful future.

You will note the "story" gets shorter as you leave pieces on the "outside." You will feel less of an emotional response. This means you are experiencing some closure and resolution.

11.   Rate your panic attacks. How severe are they?

1	2	3	4	5	6		7	8	9	10
(little anxious)			(moderately anxious)				(very anxious)			(panic)

12.   Time your episodes of panic. As you breathe (2-4), simultaneously count and look at a time piece. You will notice as the days go by the intensity and duration of panic decreases.

13.   Identify the word or sound that you make every time you experience the panic response. Change the word or sound to something comforting.

One vital precept you'll learn as you go through the program: **You have valid needs.** Part of our anxiety problems can be traced back to not meeting our own needs, whether that's self-love, healthy eating or talking through a concern with someone who understands. Part of your assignment this week is to give yourself permission to be HUMAN, not *super human.* Begin asking, *"Why do I expect more of myself than I expect of others?"* Be gentle. Be kind to YOU this week. At the same time, guard against victim thinking, *"Why me? Poor me."*

You are your safe place and safe person. You don't have to go home. **You are home.** You are fully capable of changing your negative thoughts and achieving a different response.

If you can scare yourself with your thinking, you can also soothe, comfort and reassure yourself.

Do you have questions, concerns or need support? Help is just a phone call away! Call-a-Coach 1-800-515-1133.

2-18

Lucinda's Letter

from *LESS STRESS PRESS*

Welcome to California, Lucinda! These were the words I heard over and over again in the week following my move to southern California. It also happened to be the week following the largest earthquake southern California had seen in years.

Don't Panic! It will stop. These were the words that were racing through my head as I raced toward the door of our leased southern California home. My 2-year-old son under one arm, my seven-year-old daughter and her little friend trembling under the other. *"It will be OK, just keep going,"*...I heard myself saying as one of the most devastating earthquakes California has ever experienced ripped at our new home, shattering glass and jolting everything violently, us included.

Nothing can describe the terror...the rumble, the violent shaking...surely the house would fall to the ground any minute. It was a horrifying experience...being awakened from a deep sleep at 4:31 AM by the earth roaring and gyrating. I am from Ohio. I knew nothing about earthquakes. But when you're in one...you know it. What you don't know is where to run to be safe...Is anyone really sure?

Welcome to California! Are you going to stay? When are you going back to Ohio? These were the words I heard over and over and over again in the week following the great quake. I admit, I had to think and rethink. Talk about city-wide anticipatory anxiety! Could, would, this happen again? Would we survive if it did? What if we were miles away from our children when another one hit? "What if" we couldn't get to them due to damaged roads? How will we live with this constant anticipation and what if thinking?

It was my desire to help others in the area deal with their earthquake anxiety. I was looking for some information that would help people rationalize and put things in perspective. In my diligent search for reassuring information, there really wasn't any. Yes, there could be another one. No, that wasn't the "BIG ONE." Yes, it could be more devastating...next time.

So...what do you do when no one can "fix-it," promise you it would be OK or make it go away? What do you do when there isn't any great answer or easy solution? I can only tell you what I've done. I've gotten on with it. After a greater appreciation of the moment and the many simple things in life that are so wonderful, I got back to my life. However, I took control of what I could. We prepared earthquake kits and made earthquake plans. Then...we took control of our thoughts.

This experience reminded me of a time when I was young and living by myself. I would lay awake at night and worry with intensity about someone breaking in. I was so focused on it that I would be aware of every noise, every bump. I did not sleep well. I ruined several months of my life, certainly my nights, because of this anticipatory fear of "what-if." Many people in LA are doing this now...some are still living the quake...sleeping by the doors, jumping with every light tremor...running to their families homes...while others of us are back to a quality of life again...

We had another substantial aftershock today...several actually. We put it in "perspective"...We "rationalized" that these will continue for awhile...It was a beautiful day...We went out and enjoyed some of the natural pleasures that lured us to California in the first place...it was a gorgeous January day...about 68 degrees...we headed for Malibu and the beach...we saw dolphins play...we played... we ate by the ocean at a fabulous outdoor cafe...we drove through the mountains...we lived the day to its fullest. That's all you can ask for. Sometimes it comes down to a choice to live in fear or to live in faith. If you are terrified and worrying constantly...you change nothing, control nothing and cheat yourself. Life is too precious for that. I leave you with this quote:

> *"Much of what we call evil is due entirely to the way men take phenomenon. It can so often be converted into a bracing and tonic good by a simple change of the sufferer's inner attitude from one of fear to one of fight; its sting can so often depart and turn into a relish when, after vainly seeking to shun it, we agree to face about and bear it..."*

-William James

We've decided we're staying in California

Until next time...

Lesson Notes

LESSON 3

Negative and Positive Dialogue

"When you believe it - you'll see it"

-Wayne Dyer, Ph.D.

Self Talk: The Key to Healthy Self Esteem

OBJECTIVES - Lesson 3:

* Understand that our negative thoughts create our anxiety, fear and often lead to depression.

* Understand that negative thinking is a bad habit - an addiction.

* To begin to identify the thoughts behind our feelings. To understand that a person cannot have a feeling without a thought first.

* To understand that every thought carries its own chemistry. We **feel** what we think.

* To begin to listen in to your anxious and depressive thoughts.

* To stop your old automatic responses and switch to a new language that is less scary and/or depressing.

* To understand depression is fed by distorted, negative thinking.

* To begin to replace negative, depressive thoughts and replace with compassionate, respectful, comforting thoughts.

* To see that the brain does not know the difference between an imagined scenario and a real happening. It responds as if the imagined is real.

* To recognize that this session is a cornerstone for the rest of the program.

* To change our view of "failure."

Negative dialogue is one of the most important aspects of chronic anxiety and depression. One of the reasons you stay in this condition is because of the way you talk to yourself.

- ▸ You must learn to have compassion for yourself.

- ▸ You must learn to talk yourself out of being afraid.

- ▸ You must learn to praise yourself and mean it.

- ▸ You must learn to talk to yourself in a relaxing, soothing and comfortable manner.

- ▸ You must learn to use positive dialogue instead of negative when you feel you have failed at something or done something wrong.

- ▸ You must learn how to stop negative thoughts and comments and replace them with positive ones.

Often, what puts you in an anxiety attack and keeps you in depression is the dialogue you have with yourself. Negative dialogue that can produce an attack includes:

- ▸ *"Oh, no. Here it comes again. I don't think I can take it!"*

- ▸ *"I'm feeling bad. I can't stay here much longer or I'll lose control."*

- ▸ *"What's wrong with me? Why can't I be normal?"*

- ▸ *"Everyone is going to think I'm really weird."*

- ▸ *"I feel like I'm going to pass out or go crazy."*

- ▸ *"I hate myself for being like this. I feel so weak and dependent."*

- ▸ *"I can't be alone. I'll go crazy and who will be there to help me?"*

- ▸ *"What if I..."*

Do you have questions, concerns or need support? Help is just a phone call away! Call-a-Coach 1-800-515-1133.

3-2

Negative and Positive Dialogue

Examples of Negative and Positive Statements

Negative   *"I feel so dependent and afraid. Will I ever be normal again?"*

Positive   ***"Feeling this way is just part of this condition. I am working on getting over this and I will feel normal again."***

Negative   *"I feel like I'm going to go crazy."*

Positive   ***"I know I'm not going crazy. I just feel this way because of this condition. I'm going to relax and float with it and not let it scare me."***

Negative   *"I will fail if I try that."*

Positive ,   ***"There is no such thing as failure. So what if it doesn't go just right. I'll try again and I might learn something."***

Negative   *"If anyone knew I had this condition, they would think I had a real problem."*

Positive   ***"That's not true. All this is is anxiety and everyone has that. I have a lot of good qualities that people like."***

Negative   *"What if I get in the car, start driving and have a panic attack? I could hurt someone. Who would help me?"*

Positive   ***"If I have an anxiety attack in the car, I'll just find a place to pull over and relax. Nothing's going to hurt me. It's just my agoraphobia. I won't get in an accident and I will help myself feel better."***

Negative   *"What if I got a job and my anxiety got worse? Maybe I would have to quit and that would really make me look bad."*

Positive   ***"My anxiety is not going to get worse! This is all there is. There really is no "worse." If I feel anxious, I would relax myself and talk myself out of feeling panicky. Eventually, the feelings would go away."***

Fear of Failure

What is Fear of Failure?

Basically, it is the fear of self-hate and self-rejection.

It stems from a strong need for total acceptance from self and from others. That, of course, is something we can **never** achieve. When we fail, we feel disgraced, embarrassed, depressed and unworthy of respect.

Fear of Failure is fear of rejection.

It results in decisions designed to prevent the possibility of failure and rejection - decisions that result in jobs never taken, relationships never started, opportunities left unchallenged, promotions never asked for, chances never taken and independence never achieved.

These are just a few of the possibilities for success that are "avoided" due to fear of failure.

A person with a healthy self-esteem, who has managed to find success in life, has experienced many failures along the way.

The key is to fail *successfully*, to understand that falling short is always a possibility and to recognize that it is part of the life process.

That doesn't mean you shouldn't try. It means you should keep trying until you get it right. *So what* if it takes you a little longer than the next person. *So what* if you experience a few bruises along the way.

The only way to get comfortable with the possibility of failure and rejection is to **expose** yourself to it.

By taking chances and allowing yourself to be rejected, you will come to realize that while your pride may be temporarily shaken, your real self remains unchanged. You are still that same person with the same talents and abilities. No one can change that.

Permitting the experience of rejection and failure - and gradually becoming less and less affected by it, is extremely freeing. You are then able to knock on any door, to try new experiences, to accept a challenge and to make exciting, life-fulfilling decisions. Your decisions will be made out of desire, not fear.

Do you have questions, concerns or need support? Help is just a phone call away! Call-a-Coach 1-800-515-1133.

3-4

Negative and Positive Dialogue

Homework

Name _____

What failures have you experienced in your life?

_____

_____

_____

_____

How did these experiences make you feel?

_____

_____

What could you have done differently?

_____

_____

_____

What accomplishments have you achieved in your life?

_____

_____

_____

Homework cont...

Name _____

List below any negative thoughts or statements you have had this past week. After you have written the negative statement, write a positive statement on the line below it.

Negative _____

Positive _____

Negative _____

Positive _____

Negative _____

Positive _____

Negative _____

Positive _____

Negative _____

Positive _____

Do you have questions, concerns or need support? Help is just a phone call away! Call-a-Coach 1-800-515-1133.

3-6

Negative and Positive Dialogue

Positive Statements

☻ *It's no big deal.*

☻ *I'm not anxious. I'm excited!*

☻ *It just doesn't matter.*

☻ *I'm okay. I'll be fine.*

☻ *It's just my anxiety. It will go away.*

☻ *Go for it!*

☻ *I'm taking this too seriously.*

☻ *I'm going to float with it and it **will** go away.*

☻ *It's not worth getting anxious about.*

☻ *It's their problem.*

☻ *I'm not going to take that action or comment personally.*

☻ *I'll feel better tomorrow.*

☻ *Of course I'm anxious because...*

☻ *Look how far I've come and the ways I've changed. So what if I still feel anxious.*

☻ *So what if...*

Homework Responses

This homework session is one of the most important segments in this program. Many times, if not all the time, what you think and say to yourself is what produces feelings and symptoms of anxiety.

Here's an example of a negative and a replacement statement.

> NEGATIVE - *Going out of town.*
> POSITIVE - *I'll be OK.*

First, this negative thought is too general and not a complete statement. It would be preferable to write this as, *"I am afraid to go out of town. What if these feelings happen on the trip?"* When written as a complete statement and the reason for your fear is given, it is easier to write a replacement statement.

Secondly, the positive replacement statement above is very vague, too easy and ineffective. It really does nothing to make you feel better. A preferred statement might be, *"Of course I feel anxious about going on a trip. Some of these feelings might be excitement. I need to work on this gradually, using my new skills and I will eventually feel comfortable."* See how much more comforting this is?

> NEGATIVE - *I've had this problem too long. I will never be normal again.*
> POSITIVE - *I am normal. I just have a problem with anxiety.*

This is a good example of a negative statement. Always ask yourself if you are catastrophizing or exaggerating your negative thoughts. The positive statement is fairly good. You might add a little compassion by writing, *"I am working on changing and feeling a little stronger and better every day."* You may not believe it, but eventually you will.

Here are some examples of good positive and negative statements:

> NEGATIVE - *The weather is awful today. It is making me feel more anxious.*
> POSITIVE - *It's nice for the weather to be different. I would get tired of it if it stayed the same. I can get through this anxious period.*

> NEGATIVE - *If I quit my job and fail, what will my family do?*
> POSITIVE - *(I am not going to quit unless I choose to because I am not happy.) If I do quit, this is not failure, it is a choice. There are other jobs. It may be the best thing that could happen - to get me out of my comfort zone and into something more challenging.*

Do you have questions, concerns or need support? Help is just a phone call away! Call-a-Coach 1-800-515-1133.

3-8

Homework Responses cont...

Now, here is a negative and positive statement that could be elaborated on:

> NEGATIVE - *I don't feel well in the morning.*
> POSITIVE - *It will go away.*

Why don't you feel well in the morning? These statements are too black and white. The positive statement is too simple and unbelievable. It might be more effective to say, *"It takes me a while to wake up. I am just anticipating the day ahead. I will give myself plenty of time to get up and get going. I will watch what I eat for breakfast. This will change eventually. I need to be more patient."*

The idea is to write down any negative thoughts you have **when you have them** and try to replace them with a comforting thought. Eventually you will begin to feel different. You control what you put into your brain. Make it make you feel better.

FEARS OF FAILURE

Most failures people list aren't failures at all. They are often things like bad marriages or not going to college. Possibly career related. It is never too late for anything. You may need to reevaluate these issues.

Many people say these experiences made them feel useless, sad, weak, like a failure, low self-esteem, a loser.

Many of these situations can be remedied. If you want to go back to school, you can. You can complete anything you didn't finish. You need to realize that some of these things weren't your fault and you need to forgive yourself for those that were. That is life. You learn from your mistakes.

MISTAKES ARE OPPORTUNITIES FOR GROWTH. Nothing more.

Be sure to list your accomplishments at all times. Pat yourself on the back for even the smallest achievement. Why? Because it will make you feel better. You can make you feel better.

When you have a negative, anxious and/or depressing thought, ask yourself, *"Is this thought even valid?"* It probably isn't. Imagine a big, red stop sign in your mind to stop the thought. Then replace the thought with a positive, compassionate thought. Remember, you choose your thoughts.

Think positive! You will eventually begin to believe it!

"Your belief is your biology." With every thought, there is a chemical reaction and associated physical effects. We interpret these feelings and label them with an emotion we have come to associate with those sensations.

You will find that this is one of the more important sessions in the series. This is a "hinge" lesson. Future techniques and skills depend on your ability to use those taught in this session.

For many, it is hard to believe that positive thinking could make that much difference in dealing with the symptoms of anxiety, let alone depression.

Making positive dialogue, self talk, thought talk, a natural part of our thinking process takes a lot of practice and patience. In some ways we are learning a new language. At first it will feel like you are translating everything. You may even feel awkward at times. Some of your positive thoughts may not even sound believable. Practice makes proficiency.

It sometimes helps to look at some of the cognitive distortions that lead to our negative thinking. It helps to see that specific kinds of thoughts create specific kinds of feelings.

1. **All or nothing thinking:** In this type of thinking there is no middle ground. If we make a mistake or have a bad day, we feel we are a total failure or never do anything right, rather than as just one mistake. This type of thinking is usually unrealistic since things are rarely 100% one way or another.

2. **Negative predictions or jumping to conclusions:** We predict that things will turn out negatively, often because of past experiences or emotional pain from our past. This fits our, *"I'm never going to change"* attitude, or our belief that because one person reacted negatively everyone will. *"I'll never get a date, a good job, etc...."*

3. **Filtering information negatively:** This often involves picking a negative detail and dwelling on it. The total emphasis is placed on our weight, our looks, our health, etc..., seeing only that piece. It is healthy to look at the whole picture.

    Filtering involves a tendency to disqualify the positive as well. If ten people compliment us and one person says something negative, we filter out the ten and dwell on the one negative. We need to learn to let the nice things sink in. Our dialogue needs to reflect that we are learning to be a good friend to ourselves.

Do you have questions, concerns or need support? Help is just a phone call away! Call-a-Coach 1-800-515-1133.

3-10

4.   **Mind reading:** With our negative distortions we often *assume* that others are reacting negatively toward us. Our inner dialogue leads us to believe that people are looking down on us or are angry without checking out what may really be going on. An important skill is to learn to ask what's going on instead of guessing.

5.   **Shoulds:** This type of thinking indicates things have to be a certain way. This thinking habit is so prevalent that we have devoted an entire lesson to it. This week notice this type of dialogue and write it down for next week.

   Insisting something "should" or "shouldn't" be a certain way, feel a certain way, will intensify anxiety and depression. We will learn to give ourselves permission to have certain feelings and acknowledge that a situation is upsetting or unpleasant. With practice we will then move into the problem solving mode and decide what we can DO to make a positive difference.

6.   **Overgeneralized thinking:** This includes those labels we've carried with us for so long. Listen in to your self talk. What automatic thoughts are habitually stated? What names are you calling yourself? *"I'm so stupid. I'm a loser. I deserve to feel bad."* Would you allow **anyone else** to say these things to you?

These common errors in thinking will set in motion depression and anxiety. When you begin to **hear** and be aware of your thought talk, you will understand why you are depressed and stressed.

Client: *"I can't believe what I did to myself. I had an actual asthma attack over **silk** flowers! What a lesson in the power of a thought!"*

Try to think of examples from your own experience that illustrate the mind/body connection. If we can use the mind/body connection in a negative way, we can also use it in a positive way. What might happen to your depression if you never again beat yourself up? What if you stopped saying things about yourself that you would never allow another human being to say about you? What if you discovered **optimism**?

We have the freedom to think any thought or string of thoughts, therefore, it follows that we determine how we feel. What a gigantic concept!

Present day cognitive therapy emphasizes: We have control. We determine. We are capable of living peace-filled, productive lives. We are capable of questioning, free thinking and self-determination.

Negative and Positive Dialogue

Action Assignments

1. Use your relaxation tape three times each day. Lie down for at least one of the three times.

2. Exercise aerobically each day. If you have not been exercising, work up slowly to 30-45 minutes.

3. Listen to your lesson tape on at least three different days.

4. Do the homework and action assignments throughout your week.

5. Recommended reading listed in the newsletter is very helpful.

6. Continue to cut down and eliminate stimulants.

7. Take 10 minutes each day to write about your feelings in your personal journal. Record your experiences with the action assignments.

The above seven (7) actions will be referred to in the future as "the basics" for each week.

8. Keep a small spiral notebook with you all day one day this week. Make a "tic" mark in your notebook each time you catch yourself thinking a negative thought.

9. Practice going one hour or a whole day without saying anything negative or complaining. Note your experience.

10. Practice for one day saying as many realistic, positive things about yourself and others as you possibly can. Note your experience.

11. In your journal or on a sheet of paper, make a list of at least ten positive things about you and your life.

12. If you are not sure a statement is negative, ask yourself if the thought is true. Ask, *"Is this thought reasonable, realistic or rational?"* If not, it's negative. Change it. Refocus, and tell yourself the truth.

13. At the end of this week glance over your past three weeks of journaling. Can you see any themes or patterns developing?

Client: *"I notice every Sunday evening I get more and more depressed feelings."*

Client: *"In writing I sound very angry."*

Do you have questions, concerns or need support? Help is just a phone call away! Call-a-Coach 1-800-515-1133.

3-12

Action Assignments

14.   **IMPORTANT** - If your **second** language is English, construct your positive dialogue in your **first language**.

15.   Use some of your negative thoughts to accomplish your negative to positive statements in your homework (see 3-6). Write a few others in your journal. Use the following tactics and write about what you learn about yourself and your thoughts:

Rewind - What was going through your mind right before that negative thought/feeling? What was I telling myself?

Categorize - In what style of negative thinking would this thought be listed. (see 3-10)

Disputing - Start disputing your negative thought talk as you would if you heard your son/daughter or good friend saying the same thing.

16.   Practice relaxation this week as you reframe your negative thoughts. As soon as you notice a negative thought, inhale for two seconds, exhale for four seconds. Let go and slow yourself down. Look for the truth. You are transporting yourself from a negative state to a positive one. It can be done in seconds. You are in control.

17.   At the end of week three, review tape two. When we are learning new material, repetition is very important.

18.   Write down your goal for this week.

Thought for the week:

Interrupt....Interrupt....Interrupt....refocus, restructure, replace, regroup, reevaluate, redesign....reward!

It is impossible to have positive feelings with negative thoughts.

"If you always think the way you've always thought, you'll always feel the way you've always felt. "If you always do what you've always done, you'll only get what you've always gotten."

Healthy thinking leads to healthy emotions, healthy behavior and a better life. If you want to change your life, you have to start by changing your thoughts.

Whenever you have learned something new you have had to seek instruction. Learning to think in positive, productive ways is a skill that takes instruction, guidance and practice.

"Thinking is the hardest work there is, which is the probable reason why so few engage in it."

Henry Ford

Lesson Notes

Do you have questions, concerns or need support? Help is just a phone call away! Call-a-Coach 1-800-515-1133.

3-14

SLEEPLESS IN SEATTLE, CHICAGO, NEWARK,....

by Carolyn Dickman, Education Director, Midwest Center. From *LESS STRESS PRESS*.

"There is a gulf between those who can sleep and those who cannot. It is one of the great divisions of the human race."   Iris Murdock, <u>NUNS AND SOLDIERS</u> (1980)

My father used to say my mother had a brick in her pillow so that as soon as her head hit the pillow she was asleep. Even as a small child I heard a hint of envy in his voice. He used to listen to Mitch Miller albums far into the night. How do I know? I listened too. Not because they kept me awake, but because I was glad to have the distraction-distraction from the otherwise scary scenarios I conjured up.

We were not allowed to get up once we had been put in bed. I remember being as young as seven or eight creeping on hands and knees, slowly, silently, skipping the floorboards that squeaked, to get to the landing. Our house was at least a hundred years old and the ten foot creaky mine field required at least ten or fifteen minutes to traverse. I would lie at the top of the stairs listening to my parents and the TV until I felt a bit tired. How much of our sleeplessness is learned, programmed, genetic? I don't know, but I will never say to my children, "Good night, don't let the bedbugs bite." Bed bugs!? What do they look like? How big are their teeth? And how about that "cradle will fall" stuff? Or, "Now I lay me down to sleep. I pray the Lord my soul to keep. For if I should die before I wake, I pray the Lord my soul to take." Comforting? Maybe, depending on your perception. What is that noise? "Is that you Lord?" It might not be a bad idea to examine some of the things said in jest, out of habit, about sleep.

Many of our callers ask questions about sleep, more to the point, about **not** sleeping. One of my unexpected benefits from the program, Attacking Anxiety, was a positive change in my quality and quantity of sleep. In my efforts to address this huge subject I have talked to our Medical Director, Phillip Fisher, (his outline for sleep hygiene follows), and read several books. I encourage you to do the same. (Please share with us new material you discover.) In the course of taking new, broader, more complete responsibility for my life, health, and happiness, I have seen the benefits of taking on the role of researcher, scientist and self-healer. Becoming action-oriented helps you feel more in control, less stressed, and therefore, less likely to spend another sleepless night.

Here's a bit of trivia I gathered from my readings. Only in recent history has sleep been so structured. Until the last three or four hundred years there were no bedrooms. Communal beds were the norm and if a traveler asked to spend the night he retired in the family bed-with the family. It wasn't uncommon to see people asleep at all hours, in all places.

There does seem to be a definable difference between "morning" and "night" people. It is unknown at this time if this bent is inherited or habituated, at present, data gives more weight to the genes. There are volumes written on how much sleep we need. The average, and seemingly most healthful, amount runs between seven and eight hours. We know that mood affects our sleep; those in positive moods seem to require less sleep. There are four levels of sleep. Caffeine\alcohol disturbs one of the levels. If we do not progress through each of these levels our quality of sleep will suffer.

"I didn't sleep at all last night!" We frequently hear this lament. But upon questioning it is generally found that this is an exaggeration. Such negative programming can have a profound effect. Thought talk must be addressed. Our brain has no choice but to believe what we tell it. And you will observe behavior in accordance. Not long ago I awoke at a seemingly early hour, felt very awake and rested, shuffled out to the kitchen in the morning darkness. I misinterpreted the position of the clock arms and moaned at what I thought was 3:30. "Oh, man am I tired! I hope I can go back to sleep." After roaming around for a time I glanced again at the clock and observed with less bleary eyes, 6:30. "Oh, alright-time to get moving!" In a short span of time I had gone from rested to tired, to ready for the day. The power of a thought can still astound me. If you are not sure about designing some positive dialogue regarding sleep (and other issues), please note suggestions in Helmstetter's book, <u>**WHAT TO SAY WHEN YOU TALK TO YOURSELF**</u>.

I will never forget Frances. She was in a recent group, and when she began she won the award for the most angry, negative person in the gathering. One of her major problems other than anxiety disorder and depression, was sleeping. I gave her the hints I am about to share with you, and gave her Helmstetter's book as an assignment. I told her even if she didn't believe her affirmations: "I am a great sleeper. I love my bed. I love to go to bed, and as soon as my head hits the pillow I am relaxed, calm and sleepy. I am a great sleeper. When I go to bed tonight I am going to enjoy a wonderful night's sleep," she was to say them every time she thought about sleep. She almost smacked me, but agreed to our "experiment." I can't tell you how delighted she was telling us a month later that she was sleeping.

Almost everyone experiences a night or two of poor sleep. There is no evidence that this poses any serious health threat. To be sure, the next day may be a challenge and our coping skills may not be as sharp, but our over-reaction can be our biggest downfall. Be kind and gentle to yourself in this situation. Soothe yourself with compassionate dialogue, exercise, no stimulants, purposefully under-react to everything and use your relaxation tape two or three times that day.

If you frequently suffer from sleeplessness, of course consult your care-giver, but a little detective work may uncover behavior (such as useless worry) and thought patterns that set us up for insomnia. Is there a theme to your worries? If so address it.

SLEEP HYGIENE: 1. Regular rise and fall-go to bed at the same time every evening, arise at the same time every morning regardless of how much sleep you did or didn't get. This re-sets the body's sleep clock, and humans seem to thrive on regularity. 2. A peaceful evening-leisure, relaxation, no exercise three hours before retiring, no heavy eating and use your relaxation tape. Instead of counting sheep, play your day backwards. William Walter, PhD, of the Ochsner Clinic Sleep Disorders Program in Baton Rouge, notes that insomniacs often cannot ignore background noises. Based on preliminary research he suggests that you tune your radio to static. This produces what is known as "white noise," and masks other sounds. Listen to a long-playing recording of nature sounds, waves, etc. My mother used to tell me to pray the rosary and if I didn't finish the angels would. The angels have finished many, but I suspect in addition to the comfort and power of prayer, repetition is helpful. You might wish to try a mantra, or I can send you an extra rosary! 3. No Naps!-unless your doctor or common sense dictates otherwise. 4. No Stimulants!-caffeine, alcohol, chocolate, sugars, or nicotine, all have a stimulating effect. 5. Sleep conducive environment, make your nest for sleep. Warm milk (yes, mom was right on that one-unless you are lactose intolerant), milk and turkey breast contain tryptophan, said to naturally induce relaxation. No television or reading in bedroom, if you are not asleep after twenty or thirty minutes get up and go to another part of the house to read or watch some TV. When you feel sleepy, try again, repeat until sleep. Rise at the predetermined time regardless of how little sleep you may have had. If it wasn't much, give yourself permission to have some anxiety - be gentle and use positive thought talk throughout the day.

MEDICATION FOR SLEEP: If you are considering medication for sleep it is important that you thoroughly discuss this with your doctor. Sleeping pills are potent medications. They should not be taken lightly, and only when necessity is demonstrated. This is best determined by you and your doctor. It is important to keep dosages as small as possible, and for a limited time. They seem to become less effective with prolonged use, and therefore; we need to treat the cause of sleep difficulties.

Devising a plan for sleep puts you in control (we like that!); this is pro-active rather than passive. Treatment with sleeping pills does not encourage problem solving, rather better living through chemistry. They are not a cure but a temporary relief measure. As in the case of pain, the use of medication should be considered as a first step only, to be followed with active problem solving.

"Mister Sandman bring me a dream, make it the nicest I've ever seen..." Now where did I put that brick?

"Life is under no obligation to give us what we expect."
- Margaret Mitchell

EXPECTATIONS: How to Expect Less and Get More

OBJECTIVES - Lesson 4:

* To become more effective and less affected

* To understand that our expectations are usually too high which creates much of our anxiety and depression.

* To have a more realistic view of our world and ourselves.

* To be able to set realistic goals.

* To distinguish between healthy and unhealthy "shoulds."

* To realize we are responsible for how we feel.

* To recognize over-reactive responses.

* To see the four central themes in our beliefs that lead to anxiety and depression: perfectionism, lack of assertiveness, unrealistic expectations and victim thinking.

* To recognize that our attitude, beliefs and mis-beliefs are responsible for much of our stress, anxiety and depression.

* To understand that depression is a medical condition, and very treatable. To become more comfortable with treatment choices.

Expectations and "shoulds" often go beyond yourself to everything and everyone around you.

High expectations have the potential to set you up for disappointment.

Of course, you do need to set goals and to try to achieve them.

But too often, people who suffer from chronic anxiety and depressive episodes have unrealistic expectations attached to their goals. Consequently, when and if they achieve their goals, the results do not live up to their expectations and they are disappointed. Often, they feel so overwhelmed by their expectations of that goal that they never try to achieve it for fear of failure or fear of self-hate.

If you can learn to lower your expectations to a more realistic level, even partial achievement can be viewed as an achievement.

Maybe you didn't get the job, but you did feel you did well on the interview. Next time, you WILL get the job. Maybe you didn't do all of your grocery shopping your first time out by yourself, but you **did** make it to the store. That is an achievement. Next time, you can stay longer. Maybe you won't be completely over your anxiety and depression when you leave this program. You will be much better and you will have all the tools you need to continue working on your problems until they are conquered.

Things that are worth more usually take more time in coming. They also take more effort. When you learn to lower your expectations, you will also learn patience.

People who suffer from anxiety disorder enjoy immediate gratification. The main problem with immediate gratification is that it is not long-lasting. You often don't feel you deserve it. Somewhere in the back of your mind, you feel as if you really didn't work hard enough for it. Either way, you are headed for disappointment.

By lowering your expectations, the good things that happen are always recognized while the bad things are accepted as an inevitable part of life.

You simply learn from them and move on.

Do you have questions, concerns or need support? Help is just a phone call away! Call-a-Coach 1-800-515-1133.

4-2

Read each of the following statements. The stronger you feel about the statement, the higher the number you should circle. Find the subtotals for each column, then add the subtotals to get your total score.

Step 1: **Go through the statements and circle the number that best describes your response.**

1 = I never feel this way   3 = I frequently feel this way
2 = I occasionally feel this way   4 = I almost always feel this way

1. I like to be in control at all times 1 2 3 4
2. I like things to be fair 1 2 3 4
3. I have a hard time saying "no"
   without feeling guilty 1 2 3 4
4. I like things to be perfect 1 2 3 4
5. I have high expectations of myself 1 2 3 4
6. I worry about what other people think 1 2 3 4
7. If I want something done right, I feel
   I should do it myself 1 2 3 4
8. I feel guilty easily 1 2 3 4
9. I do not like to fail 1 2 3 4
10. I feel people should listen better 1 2 3 4
11. I don't like to cause conflict 1 2 3 4
12. People don't appreciate all that I do 1 2 3 4
13. I'm not where I want to be in life 1 2 3 4
14. There is not enough time in my day 1 2 3 4
15. I don't really feel rested 1 2 3 4

Subtotal   __ __ __ __

Total of all Subtotals   _____

Step 2: Find the subtotal for each column by adding the numbers in each column. (i.e. - If you have circled three number 3's, your subtotal will be 9).

Step 3: Add the subtotals together and note your grand total. Consult the score sheet on page (v) in the introduction to score your evaluation.

Should Rule's

"Should" rules for yourself usually are easy to recognize.

They are expectations for yourself that you typically fall short of. They are usually unrealistic and not as important as you might think. It is important here to recognize why you have these particular "shoulds" and what their importance really is. Once you begin to eliminate the "shoulds" that really aren't necessary, you will find you have eliminated much of the anxiety that comes with them in the form of procrastination.

"Should" rules that you have for others or for the world around you are impossible to fulfill. This is a different way of saying, *"I deserve this or that,"* or *"It's only fair if...."* The truth of the matter is **life has no guarantees**. Nothing is fair. You don't always get what you deserve. Very often, you get things you don't think you deserve. You set goals. You plan. You work hard and hopefully you will achieve. The only real guarantee you have is that opportunity is out there for those who are willing to go after it.

One thing "should" rules will always do is to set you up for disappointment and self-hate. You will never live up to your own expectations.

You must:
- eliminate the unimportant "shoulds"
- be more compassionate toward yourself about the important "shoulds"
- eliminate or minimize many of the "shoulds" you have for others and the world around you
- don't "should" on yourself

Examples of unrealistic "shoulds" and expectations.

- I should by happy
- I should always be in control
- People should be nice to me
- I should do everything perfectly
- People should appreciate me
- I am good, so things should go right for me
- Things should be fair
- I should be liked by everyone
- Mistakes are bad
- People should treat me as I treat them
- I should not fail

Examples of unrealistic personal "shoulds."

- I should be a better parent
- I should go back to school
- I should clean the house more often
- I should be more outgoing
- I should spend more time with my parents

Do you have questions, concerns or need support? Help is just a phone call away! Call-a-Coach 1-800-515-1133.

4-4

Homework

Name _____

List below some of the "shoulds" you have for yourself.

1. _____
2. _____
3. _____

Which of these "shoulds" could you scratch through? Which are not realistic, are not important or are other people's expectations and "shoulds" for you? Try to view the remaining (valid) "shoulds" in a more realistic way. How can you turn these "shoulds" into goals to be accomplished?

What are some of your expectations of others? _____
_____
_____
_____

Are these realistic? _____

What do you feel you deserve? _____

What do you feel you have coming to you and why? _____
_____
_____
_____

What are your expectations of this program? _____
_____
_____
_____
_____

Homework continued...

Name _____

List below any negative thoughts or statements you have had this week.

After you have written the negative statement, replace it with a positive statement on the next line.

Negative _____

Positive _____

Negative _____

Positive _____

Negative _____

Positive _____

Negative _____

Positive _____

Negative _____

Positive _____

Negative _____

Positive _____

Do you have questions, concerns or need support? Help is just a phone call away! Call-a-Coach 1-800-515-1133.

4-6

Expectations

Name _____

Please use this sheet to keep track of your diet this week. Be sure to include all beverages and treats. Don't try to make it look good to please us. Be honest!

MONDAY

Breakfast _____

Lunch _____

Dinner _____

Snacks _____

TUESDAY

Breakfast _____

Lunch _____

Dinner _____

Snacks _____

WEDNESDAY

Breakfast _____

Lunch _____

Dinner _____

Snacks _____

THURSDAY

Breakfast _____

Lunch _____

Dinner _____

Snacks _____

FRIDAY

Breakfast _____

Lunch _____

Dinner _____

Snacks _____

SATURDAY

Breakfast _____

Lunch _____

Dinner _____

Snacks _____

SUNDAY

Breakfast _____

Lunch _____

Dinner _____

Snacks _____

Example Homework Responses

This homework session is to help you understand the importance of keeping your expectations realistic.

Here are some examples of non-productive "shoulds" for yourself.

"I should clean my house more." **Who says you should?**

"I should plan better meals and cook more often." **Again, who says you should? Are these two "shoulds" things you would** *like* **to do?**

"I should spend more time with my parents." **Is this your desire or theirs?**

"I should go back to college." **If you want to go back, make this a goal.**

Expectations for others set you up for disappointment. Here are some examples:

"I expect my parents to recognize my achievements." **It would be nice if they did, but you cannot control this. Realize that if they don't, it is some lack on** *their* **part, not yours. Don't take this personally.**

"I expect my husband to help more with the housework." **This is a valid expectation. You need to be assertive in asking for his help. If he doesn't help, you need to accept this about him and learn to live with it.**

"I expect my employees to do a good job." **This certainly is realistic. Are you providing them with enough training and motivation? Again, they are human. They will make mistakes, goof-off occasionally, etc.... Expect it.**

"I deserve to be treated with respect." **Yes you do. But, you won't always get it, deserved or not.**

"I should have my career better established by now." **If you feel that way then it is time to form a plan of action to get where you want to go. Are you being too hard on yourself?**

"Shoulds" and expectations about going back to school, exercising more, losing weight etc. are all valid desires, they need to be turned into goals. If your expectations come from you and they are realistic, they can be considered valid.

Now you must decide what to do with them.

Do you have questions, concerns or need support? Help is just a phone call away! Call-a-Coach 1-800-515-1133.

4-8

Depression

According to the National Institutes of Health, the symptoms of depression can include:

~ Loss of pleasure in ordinary activities, including sex
~ Decreased energy, fatigue, being "slowed down"
~ Sleep disturbances (insomnia, early morning wakening, or oversleeping)
~ Eating disturbances (loss of appetite and weight, or weight gain)
~ Feelings of guilt, worthlessness, helplessness
~ Thoughts of death or suicide, suicide attempts
~ Irritability
~ Excessive crying
~ Chronic aches and pains that don't respond to treatment

In the work place, the symptoms of depression often may be recognized by:

~ Decreased productivity
~ Morale problems
~ Lack of cooperation
~ Safety problems, accidents
~ Absenteeism
~ Frequent complaints of being tired all the time
~ Complaints of unexplained aches and pains
~ Alcohol and drug abuse

Depression takes a huge toll. It is reported that depression accounts for more days in bed than the *eight leading* chronic illnesses.

It should be of concern if you have recurring episodes of major depression. As you reflect upon your personal history of depression, you may find that you experienced depression even as a child.

Where does depression come from?

Is it a virus? This is one of the current theories being researched. More information will be provided when we have credible data.

Is it biochemical or psychological? Most experts think it is both. This may explain the high success found when medication and therapy are combined.

Is it genetic? Some kinds of depression definitely seem to be. i.e. Manic Depressive Disorder.

There are definite conditions that precipitate or seem to be a causal factor for depression.

Medical Causes

Common medical causes of depression include thyroid deficiency, neurologic disorders, head injury and cancer (even possibly before it has been diagnosed.) Other medical causes include Addison's disease, Alzheimer's disease, cerebral ischemia, Cushing's disease, Huntington's disease, Parkinson's disease, hyper-and hypothyroidism, lupus, multiple sclerosis, nutritional deficiencies, pancreatic disease, rheumatoid arthritis, stroke and viral and other infectious diseases.

Drugs

If at any time you experience depression while taking or after discontinuing any medication, inform your doctor. Some of the drugs that are known to cause depression are alcohol, amantadine, barbiturates, benzodiazepines, carbidopa, clonidine, cycloserine, estrogen and birth control pills, levodopa, methyldopa, propranolol, reserpine, vinblastine and vincristine. Drugs that cause depression after discontinuing include amphetamines, cocaine and other stimulants, steroids and narcotics.

Many medications, although very valuable under certain circumstances, are not recommended as the sole treatment for uncomplicated depression. Antianxiety medications, stimulants and sleeping pills, for example, treat some of the most obvious symptoms of depression without helping the disease. For more on this topic, refer to the very valuable WHAT YOU NEED TO KNOW ABOUT PSYCHIATRIC DRUGS, by S. C. Yudofsky, R. E. Hales, and T. Ferguson (New York: Ballantine Books, 1991).

The above information is from: ON THE EDGE OF DARKNESS, Conversations about conquering depression, by Kathy Cronkite (New York: Doubleday Books, 1994)

Do you have questions, concerns or need support? Help is just a phone call away! Call-a-Coach 1-800-515-1133.

4-10

Action Assignments

1. Do "the basics." Listen to your lesson tape at least three times this week. Watch section four of your coaching videos.

2. Continue to use your relaxation tape two or three times daily.

3. Do the workbook homework associated with lesson four.

4. Review tape two at least once.

5. This week, think in terms of goals and action. Write a plan for problem solving. Decide how you will make "it" happen.

6. Practice this week having **no** expectations of others. This includes: how they act, how they treat you, what they do or don't do or say. Note your experiences in your journal.

7. Put yourself in some small situations that are a challenge for you. (Examples: back seat of car, allowing someone else to drive, without being defensive - stand up for yourself, not using the telephone when you want to distract yourself - work through your anxiety with your skills.)

8. Buy a nice blank book as a gift to yourself. You may wish to title it: THINGS WORTH REMEMBERING.

9. Continue to journal! Your journal is a private safe haven. Its main purpose is to allow you to explore and write about your feelings. Often the act of writing and the ability to "see" your feelings leads to therapeutic insights and solutions.

    Venting on paper can leave you feeling de-programmed and uplifted. There are studies that seem to give evidence that journaling can have a positive influence on even your physical health. James W. Pennebaker, Ph.D., author of <u>EMOTIONS, DISCLOSURE AND HEALTH</u>, believes that consistent journaling alleviates stress-related conditions such as: headaches, insomnia and colds.

    Diary it out:

    ~ write about current concerns and those that keep popping up.
    ~ describe what happened and your feelings about it.
    ~ free-fall write, don't worry about penmanship, spelling or grammar.
    ~ write every day if possible, especially when you are most bothered. The rewards you get will motivate you to keep this life management skill a part of the rest of your life.

Action Assignments

~ see a physician - get a complete check up and discuss **all of your symptoms**.

~ talk things over with a friend, family member(s) or therapist.

~ probe your feelings - figure out what's troubling you and write some strategies that will help you deal with these.

~ take a break - a simple change in routine can help give you a different perspective.

~ exercise - the times that we need to care for ourselves the best are usually the times we take the least care.

~ avoid any extra stress - no big changes, don't take on any added responsibility.

10. Go to bed each night and get up each day counting your blessings! Gratitude!

11. Keep an accurate food diary.

12. Put a small sticky backed dot on your watch face. (Or something that you look at frequently throughout your day.) Each time you see the small dot remind yourself to be twice as positive as last week.

13. Pick out one incident from your past that you feel you could have handled better. Forgive yourself completely and unconditionally.

Thought for the week:

Note: Refusing to forgive oneself is quite an arrogant stance. This position places you above all others. Refusal to forgive promotes self-centered pity.

Final Comments

Recovery is all about change. Change your old misbeliefs, expectations and get a new perception of yourself, others and the world around you. With lesson number four firmly in place you **can expect** to feel less stress, depression and anxiety.

Do you have questions, concerns or need support? Help is just a phone call away! Call-a-Coach 1-800-515-1133.

4-12

Hello Everyone!

from *LESS STRESS PRESS*

Do you remember the song, *Brown-Eyed Girl?* Well, I do. As a matter of fact, just recently that very song got me through a difficult moment. Have you ever noticed that life is full of those...difficult moments that is. Well, lately I have had my share of them. Some come without warning and others drag on and nag at you, especially at night when you are trying to sleep. I hate those the most! Anyway getting back to the song. It had been a particularly stressful week for me. My mother had not been feeling well and due to her recent stroke, we were very concerned. It was constant phone calls and doctor consultations. I also was taking meeting after meeting about a talk-show concept that I had done extensive work on, and that I really feel would be tremendously successful as well as help make the world a better place. Unfortunately, more doors were being slammed than opened. According to "them," people don't want to hear about "good" things. People want to hear about negative if not disgusting things. It was exhausting for me.

Friends were visiting and we all came down with the flu. *Ugh.* Two major projects my husband had invested much time and effort in fell apart. Nothing was working the way it was "supposed to." I was worn out. I was sick. I was feeling down. What to do? At first, I tried to retreat. Pretty difficult with two-young kids and guests staying at your house. Needless to say, that didn't work. I tried sympathy from my kids. Forget it. I tried positive self-talk. I was too tired and sick, it just didn't seem to be working. *Uh oh,* I thought to myself. *What if this was it? What if I can't get back up from here? I need something to go right. I need time alone. I need someone up above to look down and help me out, you know - give me a break, make something good happen.* Yes, even I think like this at times... I guess I'm only human.

As I stood there in the bathroom picking up laundry, feeling overwhelmed about the housework that needed to be done, I popped on the radio. There it was. A blast from my past. *"Do you remember when we used to sing...sha la, la, la, la, la, la, de da de da...brown-eyed girl."* It took me back to memories of hanging at the local swimming pool flirting with the boys. Of warm summer days and bicycle rides and a simpler life. I began to dance around the bathroom. I began to sing...*sha la, la, la, la, la...* my energy went up. My heart felt happy...I sang louder. Suddenly, my beautiful brown-eyed daughter came running in full of smiles and took my hands and round and round we danced. We laughed, we sang. And before long, there I was, out of my misery and into the precious moment. Thank God.

Life is tough. Especially as we get older and people we love start to get sick, or even worse, die. And probably 95% of the time, things don't go the way you want them to and that's hard. Especially when we have done the work and know we are going in the right direction. But, that is when it is time to live in the moment, surround yourself with love and support and let go and let God.

Summer is coming. Wonderful summer. Let's get outside more. Play more. And enjoy the people in our lives more. What are you waiting for? A time when you'll feel more secure? A time when you'll feel less stressed? Forget it! Get out. Then go ahead, dance and sing. It worked for me.

...It's amazing how it rubs off on others, especially your kids.

Until next time...

Lesson Notes

LESSON 5

Diet, Nutrition & Exercise

"You are what you eat."

Eat and Exercise to Rid Yourself of Anxiety

OBJECTIVES - Lesson 5:

*   To understand that what we eat and drink can create symptoms of anxiety and depression.

*   To understand that stimulants activate stress hormones.

*   To realize regular appropriate exercise helps reduce tension and uplifts the spirit.

*   To commit to living well and feeling good.

*   To begin to take responsibility for those parts of our health that we have control of.

*   To understand the importance of doing **nothing** and spending time alone.

Diet, nutrition and exercise play a very important role in dealing with anxiety, stress and depression. What you eat affects the way you feel emotionally and physically.

Have you ever noticed how hyperactive you feel after eating sugar, drinking cola or coffee? Sugar and caffeine are strong stimulants.

On the other hand, certain types of heavy foods will make you feel tired, drained and non-energetic. That's fine if you are not working or about to begin some activity that demands a clear head and a certain amount of energy. There are natural ways to relax yourself without taking medication. Some involve the way you eat.

Exercise is also very important.

You will do much better at handling anxiety, stress, scary thoughts, depression, tiredness, nervousness, lack of self-esteem - almost everything if you start an exercise program. There is one right for you.

Before you go out and buy expensive exercise equipment or join an expensive spa, take some advice from others who have been exercising. Start out slowly, doing something you enjoy. Exercise for what it can do for you mentally. The physical benefits will come later.

Don't feel like you must exercise everyday for a certain amount of time and if you don't - you might as well do nothing.

This is untrue for people with acute anxiety. Any amount of exertion will benefit someone who is full of anxious energy. Exercise also acts as a prevention to help you from getting anxious. You will sleep better, feel better and be less anxious.

We can't force you to eat right, to practice good nutrition and to exercise. But, if you truly want to get rid of this anxiety, depression and gain self-control, you need a complete course of action. No positive dialogue will help if you have filled yourself full of sugar and caffeine.

Change your diet. Exercise. Feel good again. Take control of your life.

Do you have questions, concerns or need support? Help is just a phone call away! Call-a-Coach 1-800-515-1133.

5-2

Diet Test

Answer "yes" or "no" to the following questions.

1.	*I drink caffeine in coffee, tea or cola beverages at least once-a-day.*	yes	no
2.	*I eat pastry items such as cake, cookies or donuts three to four-times a week.*	yes	no
3.	*I eat chocolate at least once-a-week.*	yes	no
4.	*I add white sugar to my beverages or food at least once-a-day.*	yes	no
5.	*I add salt to my food most of the time.*	yes	no
6.	*I smoke cigarettes.*	yes	no
7.	*I eat snack foods such as chips, pretzels and crackers at least once-a-day.*	yes	no
8.	*I drink alcoholic beverages five-times a week.*	yes	no
9.	*I eat candy or something sweet at least once-a-day.*	yes	no

If you answered "yes" to any of the above questions, your diet is a possible reason for some of your anxious feelings.

If you answered "yes" to questions 1, 2, 4 and 9, your diet definitely is responsible for some of your anxious and depressed feelings. This is a diet high in stimulants. You must take action immediately to change these poor eating habits. You must learn to at least cut down, if not eliminate, all sweets.

Try it for one week.

You'll be amazed at how much better you feel and how much your anxiety will decrease.

Diet plays a very important role in anxiety and depression.

Many foods contain substances that will trigger a stress response in your body. These foods release hormones that increase heart-rate, blood pressure and oxygen demands. Caffeine is one of the most common.

6 oz. cup of coffee - *108 milligrams of caffeine*

6 oz. cup of tea - *90 milligrams of caffeine*

12 oz. glass of cola - *60 milligrams of caffeine*

1 oz. chocolate - *20 milligrams of caffeine*

Two hundred and fifty milligrams per day is considered excessive and can have the following effects on your system: anxiety, nervousness, irritability, diarrhea, irregular heart beats, inability to concentrate and upset stomach.

White sugar and white flour deplete important various B vitamins from your system, causing the same symptoms as listed above.

Salt causes fluid retention which will increase nervous tension and high blood pressure levels.

Although 250 milligrams of caffeine per day is the amount considered to be excessive, many people are extremely affected by a smaller amount. People who suffer from chronic anxiety can put themselves in a panic from the caffeine from one candy bar or headache pill.

Be sure to read all labels, because many foods or medicines contain caffeine.

Do you have questions, concerns or need support? Help is just a phone call away! Call-a-Coach 1-800-515-1133.

5-4

Vitamins and Minerals

This is a list of vitamins and minerals some experts feel might be beneficial to some people who are experiencing anxiety.

It is extremely important that you check with your family doctor before taking vitamin and mineral supplements because too much of either can be damaging. We are not recommending you take these vitamins. That is your decision. Again, check with your doctor, read the labels and don't take more than the recommended dosage. It would be preferable if you would meet your nutritionally dependent emotional needs by eating the proper food as opposed to taking supplements.

Vitamin B-6   emotional stress, fatigue, nervousness, irritability, depression, premenstrual tension and insomnia

Vitamin B-12   alcoholism, smoking, fatigue, depression, nervousness, forgetfulness and insomnia

Vitamin C   emotional stress, physically active, allergies, alcoholism, recovering from an illness, heavy coffee drinker and smoker

Iron   fatigue

Calcium   grouchy disposition, tension, cramping in the calves, depression, anxiety

Magnesium   anxiety, insomnia, depression, nervousness

Niacin, Folic Acid, Riboflavin

What foods to eat to get the vitamins and minerals needed

Vitamin B-12   beef, tuna

Vitamin C   orange juice, papaya, grapefruit, broccoli

Iron   spinach, roast beef, raisins, nuts, oysters

Calcium   low-fat cheese, yogurt, sardines, almonds, white beans

Vitamins and Minerals cont...

Magnesium   soybeans, almonds, tofu, seafood, whole grains, bran

Niacin   beef, white meat chicken, peanuts

Folic Acid   orange juice, brewers yeast, beef

Diet and Nutrition cont...

- reduce your consumption of high fat red meats, especially meals such as sausage and hot dogs.

- Cut back on fatty foods such as cream, butter, ice cream, pastries and cheese. Fatty foods are harder to digest. They sit in your stomach, making you uncomfortable. Fat is responsible for many physical illnesses, especially cardiovascular disease and obesity.

- Learn to enjoy the flavor of unsalted foods. Make a serious effort to avoid adding salt to your food. Do you salt your food before you even taste it? Use more spices such as garlic and pepper.

- Choose more fish and poultry - broil it instead of frying it. Take the skin off chicken. The skin contains the most fat.

- Eat no more than three eggs per week. Eggs are high in cholesterol.

- Cut down as much as possible on sweets. White sugar found in candy, cookies, soda etc...is very bad for the system. It can cause nervous, anxious feelings. Also, it can act as a depressant and, shortly after consuming it, can make you feel quite tired and rundown.

- Peas and beans are full of protein and a great source of fiber, so try adding more to your diet.

- Include raw, unprocessed bran in your daily diet. Try eating two-tablespoons of raw, unprocessed bran daily. It will regulate your bowels and minimize your chances of colon problems. It tastes best in cereal or yogurt. If you do not eat fiber now, add it gradually to your diet. Begin with just a teaspoon per day for a week, gradually increase weekly.

Do you have questions, concerns or need support? Help is just a phone call away! Call-a-Coach 1-800-515-1133.

5-6

Diet and Nutrition cont...

- Use whole wheat and grain breads and cereals.

- Develop a tolerance and appreciation of mild hunger. Think of it as a positive, light feeling, instead of a need that must be met.

- Eat your meals slowly. Always sit down and enjoy your meal. Take smaller bites of food and chew your food longer.

- Drink eight - 8 oz. glasses of water a day. Water is a cleansing agent. It also helps to control the appetite.

- Eat more fruit and less "junk" snacks. Make an effort to eat more uncooked vegetables. Uncooked, they're more nutritious, more filling and a good source of fiber.

- Eat breakfast and try to eat three meals a day. This will help to keep your blood sugar balanced.

- Make sure you take in a good amount of calcium daily. Calcium is thought to have a soothing, calming effect on the nervous system. Calcium can be found in yogurt, low-fat milk and cheese, cottage cheese and calcium supplements.

- Drink fruit juice between meals instead of soda. It will keep your energy level up and help you to maintain normal blood sugar levels.

- Avoid caffeine and sweets before bed time. Try to make your evening meal a light meal. You will sleep much better.

- Take vitamins with meals. They are usually more effective with food in your stomach.

Foods that affect your moods

Foods that uplift: protein: lean beef, chicken without skin, fish, peanut butter, cottage cheese, yogurt, cheese (dairy products should be low-fat), peas, beans, soy milk and tofu.

Foods that calm: carbohydrates: whole grain breads/crackers, corn, pasta, potatoes and rice (especially brown rice).

Low fat, high protein breakfasts make you feel energetic. Fatty breakfasts make you feel tired.

For those late afternoon doldrums at work, try eating protein.

Frozen vegetables contain almost as many nutrients as fresh vegetables. When you cannot buy fresh vegetables, buy frozen vegetables. If using canned vegetables, be sure to consume the liquid - it contains the nutrients.

Cutting back on cholesterol

Cut back on meat, poultry with the skin and fat, whole dairy products, palm oils, coconut oils (found in crackers), cookies and non-dairy creamers. Read the labels.

Use unsaturated fat cooking oils - corn, olive, canola, safflower, sesame, soybean and sunflower. Stay clear of fried foods.

Your total intake of cholesterol should be less than 300 mg. a day. One egg yolk contains 250 mg.

Pre-menstrual syndrome

Increase intake of magnesium by eating vegetables, seafood, nuts, cereals (no sugar), grains and low-fat dairy products.

B-6. No more than 100 milligrams a day and taken only 10-days prior to menstrual cycle. Once period begins, discontinue.

Avoid salt, caffeine, sugar, chocolate and alcohol.

Do you have questions, concerns or need support? Help is just a phone call away! Call-a-Coach 1-800-515-1133.

5-8

Diet, Nutrition & Exercise

Exercise...Questions to ask yourself:

❖   *Do I need a routine or am I one who prefers spontaneity?* Would you do better with a scheduled exercise program or exercising when you feel like it?

❖   *Do I feel more comfortable exercising alone?* It gives you time to think and reflect. Also, you don't worry about smelling or looking bad.

❖   *Am I someone who needs a push, who needs to be motivated?* Then, would you do better exercising with someone?

❖   *Do I have a hard time getting up in the morning?* If so, maybe you'd do better exercising in the evening.

❖   *Do I have more anxiety and stress when I wake up or at the end of the day?* Exercising will alleviate this anxiety.

❖   *Do I prefer getting out of the house or would it be more convenient to exercise at home?*

❖   *What type of activity do I most enjoy - riding a bicycle, dancing, swimming, walking, running or jumping rope?*

The five basics of aerobic exercise

Walking. Running. Swimming. Cycling. Skipping rope.

> -if you have strong legs, try cycling
> -if you are well-coordinated and quick on your feet, try skipping rope
> -if you swim well, then swim
> -if you are in fairly good health and have strong bones, try running
> -if you are overweight, start with walking two-miles per hour, working up to four-miles
> per hour

These are good because they will allow your body to expend enough energy to reach and sustain your heart's target zone without strain.

Figuring target rate: subtract your age from 220, multiply by .75. {i.e. 220 - 54 yrs old = 166 x .75 = 124 beats/min.} This is the heart rate that you want to work up to and eventually maintain for 20 minutes. (Five minute warm-up, 20 minute work out, five minute cool down). Check with your physician to be sure this is appropriate for your present level of health.

Making sure you enjoy what you do so you will continue. Start slowly - once a week, to twice a week, to three times a week. Exercise before you eat and you will eat less. The key to exercise is to *just do it!*

Name _____

Please use this sheet to plan your diet this week. Make a little effort to eat foods that will make you feel better. After you list what you will eat, list why you are eating this. At the end of the week, go back through the list and add whatever else you ate and cross out what you did not eat.

MONDAY
Breakfast _____
Lunch _____
Dinner _____
Snacks _____

TUESDAY
Breakfast _____
Lunch _____
Dinner _____
Snacks _____

WEDNESDAY
Breakfast _____
Lunch _____
Dinner _____
Snacks _____

THURSDAY
Breakfast _____
Lunch _____
Dinner _____
Snacks _____

FRIDAY
Breakfast _____
Lunch _____
Dinner _____
Snacks _____

SATURDAY
Breakfast _____
Lunch _____
Dinner _____
Snacks _____

SUNDAY
Breakfast _____
Lunch _____
Dinner _____
Snacks _____

Do you have questions, concerns or need support? Help is just a phone call away! Call-a-Coach 1-800-515-1133.

Name _____

Please use this sheet to record your exercise for this week. Yes, this means you must begin an exercise plan. List the activity and how much time you spent at it. Example: walking - 15 minutes, sit-up's 20.

MONDAY _____

_____

_____

TUESDAY _____

_____

_____

WEDNESDAY _____

_____

_____

THURSDAY _____

_____

_____

FRIDAY _____

_____

_____

SATURDAY _____

_____

_____

SUNDAY _____

_____

_____

GOOD FOR YOU! Now, continue this plan throughout the rest of the program and be sure to alternate exercises so you do not get bored. Remember, they get easier the more you do them!

EXAMPLE OF A BAD DIET

Name   Greg Small

MONDAY
Breakfast - 2 cups coffee, 1 bowl Frosted Flakes
Lunch - 2 cheeseburgers, fries, cola
1 candy bar in afternoon
Dinner - fried chicken, rolls, mashed potatoes, pie with cream

TUESDAY
Breakfast - none, coffee
Lunch - 2 cheeseburgers, apple pie, cola
Dinner - 2 hot dogs, potato chips, 2 alcoholic drinks

WEDNESDAY
Breakfast - 2 cups coffee, jelly, roll
Lunch - pizza, ice-cream soda
Dinner - steak, scalloped potatoes, 2 cups coffee

THURSDAY
Breakfast - 2 cups coffee, muffin with egg and cheese
Lunch - taco salad, cola
Dinner - snacks, chips, donut, bologna sandwich, 2 alcoholic drinks

FRIDAY
Breakfast - none, coffee
Lunch - 2 cheeseburgers, fries, pie candy bar
Dinner - Mexican food, enchiladas, beer

SATURDAY
Breakfast - bowl of cereal, 2 cups coffee
Lunch - none
Snacks - candy bar, chips
Dinner - fish, potatoes, salad, 1 drink alcohol

SUNDAY
Breakfast - 2 eggs, 2 pieces of toast, 2 cups coffee
Lunch - bacon, lettuce, tomato sandwich, orange juice
Dinner - spaghetti, bread, cake

This person is eating too much junk and too much sugar! Alcohol should by minimized! This person is drinking too much alcohol - caffeine is a problem here too.

A few selections are fine, but overall, this really is not a healthy diet. This person needs to become more aware how his diet affects his moods. Orange juice or any juice concentrate contains more sugar. Eat a piece of fruit.

Do you have questions, concerns or need support? Help is just a phone call away! Call-a-Coach 1-800-515-1133.

Diet, Nutrition & Exercise

EXAMPLE OF A GOOD DIET

Name _____ Sue Jones

MONDAY

Breakfast - unsugared cereal, decaf coffee
Lunch - salad, whole wheat bread
Dinner - skinned chicken, vegetable, potato
Snack - homemade or box-made bran muffins

TUESDAY

Breakfast - 1 cup yogurt, 2 tablespoons bran, decaf coffee
Lunch - tuna salad sandwich, sugar free cola, water
Dinner - spaghetti, bread, 2% milk
Snack - fruit salad

WEDNESDAY

Breakfast - 2 pieces whole wheat toast, sliced melon, decaf
Lunch - broiled fish, vegetable salad, sherbert
Dinner - shiskebob with rice, spring water

THURSDAY

Breakfast - 2 egg omelet, 1 slice whole wheat toast, decaf
Lunch - 1/2 cup cottage cheese, sliced tomatoes, whole wheat bread
Dinner - grilled cheeseburger, french fried potatoes

FRIDAY

Breakfast - bowl of oatmeal, strawberries, decaf
Lunch - broiled shrimp, cole slaw, carrots, decaf
Dinner - pork chops, broccoli, mashed potatoes
Snack - small dish (1-scoop) vanilla ice cream

SATURDAY

Breakfast - bran muffin, banana, decaf
Lunch - salad, sprite
Dinner - pizza, 1-beer, caffeine-free soda

SUNDAY

Breakfast - pancakes (light on syrup), decaf
Lunch - club sandwich on whole wheat
Dinner - small tenderloin steak, baked potato, vegetable

Sue is eating a <u>fairly</u> good diet. She is avoiding caffeine and sugar as much as possible except for an occasional treat.

- use sugar substitutes when possible
- use margarine as a substitute for butter
- take the skin off chicken

- eat carbohydrates
- eat fewer fatty foods
- use bran in your diet whenever possible

Protein is the most important part of our diet when it comes to maintaining good blood sugar levels, which is very important when it comes to PMS and anxiety. It is especially important at breakfast for many people.

OVER-EATING

Everyone at times feels out of control with food consumption. Maybe we reach in that bag of cookies with the resolution, *"just one."* Ten minutes later we are renegotiating. This is not a problem unless we behave this way on a regular basis and the behavior begins to interfere with our daily life and resolve to be well.

We eat for many reasons: to give our body fuel, a boost in energy, as a part of socializing with family and friends or because we are genuinely hungry.

There is one other way we use food and this can be problematic. We eat to fill emotional needs. We may eat to celebrate, to mask feelings, to decrease anger, fear, sadness, anxiety or depression.

When we begin to use food as a way to get through life's ups and downs, we are not behaving much differently than the self-medicator who uses alcohol. (It has been said that we are all "alcoholic" about something.) The problem: the "fix" is temporary. In addition there is a rebound effect; we need more of our "fix" to soothe the guilt, depression, shame and anxiety that comes with the recognition of our inappropriate behavior. Lastly, eating to deaden feelings solves **nothing** in the long run. When we avoid dealing with our "stuff" - we are doomed to dealing with-NOT dealing.

There are a number of strategies you can begin this week. First, confess. Make an appointment with your health care provider and discuss your behavior with food and any other substance you are using improperly. The first step to any change is acknowledging the truth. With your doctor's help, establish a REALISTIC weight for you. Next, design a written plan to reduce stress; this plan must include exercise.

NOT EATING

What often happens when we add depression to anxiousness is loss of appetite. One client reports: *"One week I was so nauseous from anxiety and depression I lost ten pounds. I forced myself to eat a quarter of an orange every day. Even that small amount caused me to gag. This on top of the lump in my throat and the fear that I wouldn't be able to swallow, was almost too much to bear."*

Do you have questions, concerns or need support? Help is just a phone call away! Call-a-Coach 1-800-515-1133.

5-14

For some, the most minor of down feelings are followed by nausea and losing the desire to eat. If there is no fever and it lasts for more than two or three days, we need to see our family physician.

It is very important that we stay hydrated-drink your eight glasses of water. Depending on what directives your doctor gives, try adding one-half cup of fruit juice to some of your water, drink a couple of the supplemental liquid drinks available, fresh squeezed papaya juice is reported to soothe nausea.

EXERCISE

If the benefits of exercise came in a bottle, if there were a prescription that gave its benefits, the prescriber would be wealthy beyond numbers. Exercise, one of the most healthful, helpful things we can do for stress, anxiety, depression and overall wellness, is resisted by most people. What is it about working that has become so obnoxious?

JUST DO IT! After talking with your doctor, just take that first step. If you only walk for five minutes, it's a start. Resolve:

"Tomorrow morning upon awakening, no matter how much I don't want to, am too tired, depressed, shaky, scared.... I will sit up, dress, put on walking shoes and get outside. I will walk for five minutes and then decide if I want to walk a bit further, faster..."

Those with physical limitations: use your creativity to formulate a workable regime. For example: If you cannot use your legs, turn on some classical, energizing music and conduct with your arms until you break a sweat. (Consult your doctor before beginning any exercise program.)

KEEP QUITTING

There is nothing good about smoking! We wish we could just say that and everyone would STOP. However, nicotine is one of the most addictive substances we can put into our bodies and we know it is extremely difficult to quit. Do whatever you must, but quit and keep on quitting.

People tell us that they smoke because it relaxes them. The truth is, what's relaxing is the deep breathing--unfortunately you are inhaling poisons with your deep breathing. Cigarettes are filled with chemicals that bring agitation and nervousness. Chemically they are not relaxing. Some of the chemicals go directly and instantly to the energy centers in our brain. This is why nighttime smokers do not sleep as deeply and peacefully.

KEEP QUITTING cont...

Talk with a kind doctor about your addiction. Research every option you have for quitting. Then, begin.

SUBSTANCE ABUSE

Whether your crutch is alcohol, food, sex, over the counter medication or street drugs, you must begin to see your unhealthy ways of dealing with life's stressors are not working and may very well hurt you.

If you need help with an addiction talk with family, friends, church community, medical personal and God. You don't have to do everything the hard way. Be compassionate but firm if you know you are using substances to avoid dealing with life.

FEED YOUR MIND

Treat yourself like you would a beloved friend. You wouldn't verbally abuse a friend. Kindness and compassion are words to live by. When we are respectful of ourselves, our esteem/respect for self rises. We are calmer, more at peace and that spells: l-e-s-s s-t-r-e-s-s.

FEED YOUR SPIRIT

The "how" is up to you. Mind, body, spirit...we are connected. There is no place where one stops and the other begins. When depression is strong, we often feel alone - remember **Who** carries you when you can't walk.

Thought for the week:

Shine a light on it! Repression leads to depression. Not wanting to feel and deal with life's challenges is unhealthy. Illuminate and Eliminate!

Do you have questions, concerns or need support? Help is just a phone call away! Call-a-Coach 1-800-515-1133.

5-16

LESSON 5

Diet, Nutrition & Exercise

ACTION ASSIGNMENTS

1.   Cut back on caffeine and sugar.

2.   Decide what your exercise plan will be and get started. (Using what you learned in session four--**be realistic**.)

3.   Begin cutting back on junk food and foods high in fat.

4.   Start drinking 6-8 glasses of water daily.

5.   **Gradually** begin to add raw, unprocessed bran to your diet. Introduce your body to bran gently: *week one* - 2 tsp./day, *week 2* - 1 heaping tablespoon/day, *week 3* - 2 heaping tablespoons/day, *week 4* - 3 tablespoons/day. The suggested amounts may vary if you already include 5-6 servings of fruits and vegetables, in addition to grains. Use your common sense and consult with your doctor.

6.   Don't miss an opportunity to speak and think positively. *"I deserve to be healthy. I am a great problem solver. My heart is getting stronger with each step. I deserve to be treated well. I am filled with self-respect."*

7.   A mantra style of self-talk is sometimes very effective and helpful. With each movement for the first five minutes of exercise repeat, *"Healthy!"* Repeat over and over. Or take a number of positive words and use a new one for each step/movement, *"healthy... strong... worthy... deserving... healthy... muscles... self-respect... value... stamina... freedom..."*

Note: Positive affirmations while exercising will be a distraction if you have some fears about exercising. At the same time you will be re-programming yourself.

8.   Play the relaxation tape while eating lunch.

9.   Slow down! If you are a *speedy-eddy*, slow down everything you do: walk, talk, eat etc...*slow*. If you find yourself plodding, always looking down, look up and make your movements more brisk.

10.   Assess your food diary this week; compare it to last week's diary. Be honest! Did you cut down on fats, sugars and caffeine? Did you include 5-6 servings of fruits and vegetables? Water?

11.   Consult your doctor and/or dietician if you are motivated to learn more about good nutrition and healthy exercise.

12.   Write about your feelings, your diet changes, your activity changes in your journal.

13.   Write down your goal for this week:

Final Comments

By eating less sugar and not drinking caffeine, you will feel less anxious. By exercising daily you will feel less stressed and less depressed. These things work! Give yourself four weeks to adjust to the new behaviors. You will feel better and you'll feel more in control.

We are responsible for those parts of our health that we have control of. *"Our brain controls **all** of our organs. Your stomach doesn't have a brain...you decide."*   **Dr. Fisher, M.D.**

We deserve to be treated with love and respect. How are **you** treating yourself?

Do you have questions, concerns or need support? Help is just a phone call away! Call-a-Coach 1-800-515-1133.

5-18

Lucinda's Letter

Hello Everyone!   (from *LESS STRESS PRESS*)

Why is it when we most need to take care of ourselves, we find it such a struggle to do so? I wonder how many of you are still drinking caffeine, eating sugar and chocolate, not exercising the way you should be and wondering why you feel bad?

What makes me think about this you ask? Simple. Just recently I was going 90 mph in five-hundred directions trying to take care of everything and everyone. I know I should know better, but I'm human too. I have kids, a career, a mother who became seriously ill and needed a lot of my time and a book tour to complete. As a result of the hectic schedule, I found myself drinking an occasional coffee. The occasional coffee turned in to a cup of coffee every morning for about a month. Also, I wasn't able to exercise like I normally do because of a totally insane travel schedule. I guess I should say I "didn't take the time to exercise," but when you fly on three planes in one day it gets pretty crazy.

So, what's my point here? When things finally stabilized and I tried to get back into my "healthy routine," I couldn't believe how hard it was and how bad I felt! For starters, going back off the daily cup of coffee was really awful. I felt tired, grouchy and had bad headaches for several days. It took days to get my energy level back up. Getting back into my four-mile walk up the mountain took some effort too. At first, I felt out of breath and had sore knees. What was really interesting though, my overall mood during this hectic period. I was just tired, irritable and not myself. So here I was at a time in my life when I really needed to take care of me and instead, I was taking care of everything but me. And I suffered for it.

As I got off the coffee and got back into my exercise routine, I began to feel peaceful again. It took about a week of feeling bad before I began to feel good. You might be wondering what the difference is in the way I feel when I'm on the "right" routine: just calmness and balanced energy throughout the day. I sleep well and feel less "on edge." When I drink coffee and eat sugar, I can definitely feel the edge. It is a slightly irritable, less patient, slightly anxious edge. Also, I don't sleep well and wake up early, around 5:00 am. All that just from one-cup of coffee! We think to ourselves, "*It's just one cup of coffee, that's no big deal.*" But one cup of coffee is addictive! And what about those of us who follow up later in the day with a coke or an iced-tea? It's so easy to fall into.

What this all shows me is how sensitive we are. We are sensitive to so many things - caffeine, sugar, chocolate, alcohol, medications - lack of exercise. It doesn't mean we can't eat chocolate or drink coffee, it simply means that we will probably pay a price. If we want to feel out ultimate best we should try to minimize and preferably eliminate stimulants and exercise every day. I talk to people all the time who tell me they still don't feel the way they want to feel and they also tell me they aren't exercising and they drink caffeine.

I challenge you to take real responsibility for the way you feel. Try it for just two weeks. Stop all stimulants and start exercising every day. Just get out and walk. You will not believe how much better you will feel at the end of the two-week period. Be prepared to feel bad for a few days. When you feel bad, you know you are addicted to the caffeine or sugar. But, be patient and get out and exercise and you will slowly begin to feel better. Eventually, you will feel better than you've felt in a long time.

Well, that's it for this newsletter. Here's to a less anxious, more relaxed life...the choices are ours, let's make healthy ones.

Good Luck!

Vitamins

By **Phillip Fisher, M.D.**, Medical Director and Co-founder of The Midwest Center for Stress and Anxiety. From *LESS STRESS PRESS*

Vitamins are essential to human life. They help regulate the metabolism and assist in the breakdown of food products that release energy into our system. They form the foundation of all bodily functions and help activate the chemical reactions that are constantly taking place in the human body. Vitamins are classified as either water- soluble, which must be taken in daily because they are unable to be stored in the body, these include vitamin C and the B- complex vitamins. Fat-soluble vitamins can be stored for some length of time in the body and include vitamins A, E, D,and K.

Recommended daily allowance was instituted over forty years ago by the U. S. Food and Nutrition Board to determine a minimum dose of vitamins that would prevent disease. However, the amounts they gave us are the bare minimum that fight off such diseases as rickets, scurvy and beriberi. What they did not account for was the amount of vitamins necessary to maintain maximal health.

Although synthetic vitamins are identical to naturally occurring vitamins found in nature, they often times contain preservatives, sugar, starch, as well as other additives that the buyer should be aware of. It is well known that vitamins and minerals bonded to proteins are better absorbed and utilized and retained in the tissues more efficiently than supplements that are not bonded to proteins.

Vitamins come in many different strengths and forms and it is almost a necessity to speak with someone who is an expert in the area or to go to your local library to find out what dosages may be appropriate for you. If you have a particular medical condition, often times, certain groups of vitamins can be very beneficial when taken in conjunction with your doctor's treatment program. As a group the B vitamins help maintain healthy skin, eyes, hair, muscle tone and intestinal function. Some such as thiamin, enhance circulation and assist in carbohydrate metabolism. Riboflavin is necessary for cell formation, antibody production and growth. Vitamin B-3 is necessary for proper circulation and healthy skin as well as aiding in the function of the nervous system and metabolism of fats, carbohydrates and proteins. B-5 helps produce vital steroid and cortisone hormones from the adrenal gland. B-6 helps maintain sodium potassium balance and is required by the nervous system. Vitamin B-12 is necessary to help prevent anemia. Vitamin E is a powerful antioxidant required for tissue growth and repair. It works in concert with Vitamin C as an antioxidant vitamin combination which may have protective effects on the human heart. Vitamin A, taken in the form of beta-carotene, helps prevent night blindness as well enhancing immunity and may have some role in cancer prevention as well.

The above information is intended to be a very brief overview of vitamins and their functions. Dosages vary widely due to the uniqueness of individuals.

Below is a table that lists recommended dosages of certain vitamins. Before using any supplements you should absolutely speak with your physician for his recommended dosage and usage suggestions.

Beta-carotene	15,000 units
Vitamin A	10,000 units
Vitamin D	400 units
Vitamin E	400-600 units
Vitamin K	100 mcg.
Vitamin C	3000 mcg.

Bioflavinoids	500 mg.
B-1	25-50 mg.
B-2	25-50 mg.
Niacin	50-100 mg.
niacinamide	50-100 mg.
Pantothenic Acid (Vitamin B-5)	50-100 mg.
Vitamin B-6	25-50 mg.
B-12	300 mcg.
Chromium	150 mcg.
Iron	18 mg.
Copper	3 mg.
Zinc	30 mg.
Selenium	100-200 mcg.
Calcium	1000 mg.

Vitamins should always be taken with meals, preferably divided into at least three daily doses.

Vitamins do not make up for poor eating habits. Optimal health cannot be achieved by eating poorly and then supplementing with vitamins. It requires a total program of heathy food intake, exercise and vitamin supplementation.

Suggested Health Enhancing Daily Regimen For The Average Person.

Lesson Notes

LESSON 6

ANGER

"Anger hides fear...deal with the fear."

Stop Being Angry and Control Your Mood Swings

OBJECTIVES - Lesson 6:

* To be able to evaluate your anger and see the relationship between anxiety, depression and anger.

* To begin to break the bad habit of anger.

* To learn how to think before you react.

* To recognize that beneath most anger we find fear.

* To become less affected and more effective.

* To understand that anger can be depressing when turned inward.

* To focus on the end result, resolve or dissolve.

People who suffer with anxiety and depression are easily irritated. They tend to over-react to life's typical frustrations and disappointments.

People with acute anxiety often harbor feelings of anger and resentment that can lead to hours, days and weeks of inner and outer bitterness.

If you recognize yourself as someone who is easily irritated, there are several points you should consider about your anger before you react:

☹   Stop and think before you react. What outcome do you really want from the situation? Do you want to make someone else feel bad too? Or, do you want them to understand that you are hurt and need to discuss the issue to get it cleared up so you feel better?

☹   Is your anger useful? Is it going to help you achieve a productive result? Or, is it going to make you feel bad or negative and not really solve anything?

☹   Was the person who hurt you doing it out of some inner problem they were dealing with? Or were they really angry with you?

☹   Are you angered over a situation that you cannot change? If so, wouldn't it be better to try to ignore it and not be so affected by it?

☹   If you are staying angry at someone hoping to make them feel bad, are you *really* affecting *their* mood? Or are you just prolonging your *own* bad feelings and unhappiness?

Do you have questions, concerns or need support? Help is just a phone call away! Call-a-Coach 1-800-515-1133.

6-2

Carefully read each of the following statements. Then, put the number in the blank space that best describes your reaction to the statement.

0 - you would feel little or no anger
1 - you would feel slightly irritated
2 - you would feel moderately irritated
3 - you would feel quite upset
4 - you would feel extremely angry

◆ Someone blames you for something you did not do. _____
◆ Someone borrows something from you and damages it. _____
◆ Someone crowds in front of you in line. _____
◆ Someone driving in front of you is going very slow and you are late for an appointment. _____
◆ Someone deliberately tries to make you feel guilty for something you did or didn't do. _____
◆ Someone says something to someone else about you that isn't true. _____
◆ You forgot something in the house and you have to go back for it. _____
◆ A relative whose birthday you always remember forgets your birthday. _____
◆ You spill red wine on a new pair of pants and it doesn't come out. _____
◆ Someone tries to tell you what you are thinking or feeling. _____
◆ Someone teases you or makes a joke about you. _____
◆ A person you care very much for is insensitive about something very important to you. _____
◆ Someone takes credit for something you did. _____
◆ Someone tries to make you feel inferior to them. _____
◆ After an exhausting day at work, you find your car won't start. _____
◆ You plan to meet a friend for dinner and he or she does not show up. _____
◆ Someone you feel you've always been fair with doesn't treat you fairly. _____
◆ A pushy salesperson at the department store won't leave you alone. _____
◆ You get a speeding ticket for going five miles over the limit. _____
◆ Someone dents your brand new car in the parking lot and does not leave you a note. _____
◆ You go on a vacation to the beach and it rains the whole time. _____
◆ Someone insults you and deliberately tries to make you feel bad. _____
◆ In traveling a distance by car, you realize you have gone a half-hour out of your way and you have to turn around. _____
◆ You do something nice for someone and they fail to recognize or appreciate the gesture. _____
◆ Someone you are trying to converse with keeps insisting that he or she knows it all. _____
◆ Someone you are depending on for something you consider important doesn't come through for you. _____

Scoring

Check your score against the following:

0-26   You have a very high tolerance level. You are not easily angered. This can be healthy unless you do not feel anger because you think anger is bad or because you feel you do not have the right to show your anger. If you *choose* not to be angry because you *choose* not to react that way that is fine. However, if you choose not to show your anger because people might not like you or your anger frightens you, that is not fine. You have a right to your anger.

27-40   You are less angry than most people - probably because you choose not to make a big deal out of something that might upset someone else. You realize that life has its ups and downs and nothing is that upsetting to you. You are not one to stay angry for long.

41-60   You can get angry fairly easily. Sometimes it depends on your mood and physical health. You might work at trying to under-react to situations that you have no control over anyway. When you choose to be less affected, you choose to be less angry. You will feel a pleasant sense of control and you will feel better emotionally.

61-96   If you scored over 60, chances are good that you find yourself angry quite often. You are easily annoyed and tend to see yourself as a victim much of the time. You are choosing this misery. You choose to react this way. You can choose to be less affected. You need to work on managing your anger and you should have plenty of opportunities.

Do you have questions, concerns or need support? Help is just a phone call away! Call-a-Coach 1-800-515-1133.

6-4

Name _____

List two-examples of when someone or something made you feel angry. Then, answer the following questions.

> ‣ How did you respond to the situation?
> ‣ What results were you hoping for? Did you get them?
> ‣ How could you have been more effective and less affected?

1. _____

_____

_____

_____

_____

_____

_____

_____

2. _____

_____

_____

_____

_____

_____

Example Homework Responses

Examples of how someone or something made you angry and possible responses:

"My mother makes me angry. She constantly treats me like a child. She criticizes me constantly."

> ***"I have told myself this is the way she is and she is not going to change. I told her in a controlled tone of voice that I didn't appreciate her remarks. She seemed shocked. I felt guilty at first, but I felt better and stronger for it."***

"I went to the pharmacy to get a prescription filled and the pharmacist couldn't fill it because his computer was down. I got angry."

> ***"I should have just relaxed and returned later. There really was nothing he could do. I over-reacted and made myself upset about something over which I had no control."***

"My husband was making fun of my haircut. I reacted by defending myself. I think that is what he wanted me to do."

> ***"I should have just laughed with him and walked away. He would have let go of it and I wouldn't still be angry. It ruined my whole week. I guess his joking made me wonder if it really did look bad. I liked the cut until he made fun of it."***

"The township cut down a tree that was on township land near my house. I raked the leaves from that tree and mowed the grass beside it. Before I came home from work, a neighbor who lives three houses down took all the wood from the tree for firewood. I also have a fireplace and it was my intention to take the wood. I talked with the neighbor and told him I thought he might have asked me before he took all the wood. He did not offer to share any wood and I think I made an enemy."

> ***"I guess I need to realize that the wood really didn't belong to either of us and he simply and selfishly - in my opinion - beat me to all of the wood. The fact that he didn't offer me any wood makes me think less of him. I am going to let go of the anger. It makes him seem rather petty. He has the wood but he also has a problem."***

Do you have questions, concerns or need support? Help is just a phone call away! Call-a-Coach 1-800-515-1133.

6-6

Depression

Anger sows weed seeds in every part of our mind, body and spirit. Of all the human emotions, anger is potentially the most dangerous to our health. Until we learn to dig out the roots, anger is a choking ground cover that thwarts happiness, leads to physical illness and emotional stunting.

Again, it all begins with our thoughts. Most hostile feelings begin with inappropriate, incorrect, thoughts about other people or situations that can't be changed.

For a number of years, depression was thought to be anger turned in on oneself. We now know there are lots of other causes for depression. However, unexpressed appropriate anger, or not knowing the healthy use of this normal but powerful emotion, still ranks high as an underlying factor in some depressions.

It is important to recognize that if we "stuff" any emotion, be it anger or sadness, we are setting ourselves up for depression. Some of us were taught that anger isn't "allowed," it's not "nice." Some of us haven't "allowed" it for years, and we've never had the practice that we need in order to deal with it in a healthy manner.

Another important insight, depressed individuals do not feel good! Depression is very painful. If you have observed yourself in an over-reactive rage, yes, you must change this, but you must also give yourself a break. People who do not feel well, physically and/or emotionally, are understandably short tempered.

Beating yourself up will only further pave the way to depression. Let's face it...if beating yourself up worked, you would be happy and peaceful by now.

Anxious people over-react to EVERYTHING. When you feel the first flush of anger, step back mentally and look for the over-reactive part and fix just that much. Rage behavior is very negative and depressing because it affects your self-respect.

Integrating everything you have learned so far with what you have learned this week will further inoculate you from unnecessary, stress, anxiety and depression.

Action Assignments

1. Listen to your lesson tape at least three times. Watch Lesson 6 of your Coaching Videos.

2. Continue to listen to your relaxation tape at least twice daily. This week every time you feel the beginnings of anger or frustration, picture the relaxation tape in your mind's eye.

3. This week you are encouraged to observe your body when you feel angry. Watch others when they are angry. Do the homework in this workbook and write about your experiences in your journal.

4. When you decide you need a cooling off period, listen to your relaxation tape and then do some strategy work on paper.

5. Practice this week being less angry:
    a. Make a conscious decision to be less affected.
    b. Take a time out before responding. Breathe!
    c. Assess: Is the situation worth affecting your immune system?
    d. Allow yourself time to defuse.
    e. Ask yourself how you could under-react to the situation.

6. This week, do not raise your voice. Stay calm. Practice self-control. Note your experience. When was this most challenging? Can you see a theme to your episodes of anger?

7. This week, don't let anyone "push your buttons." Prepare for this by being aware of the people that are usually able to do this.

8. Begin to look behind your anger. Write down what else you are feeling besides anger.

9. Write about your "old" anger. Do not reread, throw it away.

10. Review tape three this week.

11. Continue your exercise efforts and healthy eating habits.

12. Discuss one of your anger reactions with a respected friend. This may give you a different perspective. Hint: When asking for advice, listen, don't defend.

13. Does old anger, new anger, anger directed at yourself, cause depressed feelings? Why?

14. Read something about forgiveness this week.

15. Write down your goals for this week.

Do you have questions, concerns or need support? Help is just a phone call away! Call-a-Coach 1-800-515-1133.

6-8

Anger is not "bad." Anger is a human emotion, but most do not know how to use it in a productive, healthy way. As you evolve into the confident, in control, person you are becoming, you will see that there are really very few things worth the price you pay when you choose to be angry. Remember **you choose**.

As you become less angry, less often, you will see a definite difference in your stress and anxiety level. You will feel more peaceful and centered. You will be in control, rather than being at the mercy of your emotions. At the same time you will begin to not only feel healthier, but *be* healthier.

Conquering hostility requires total commitment, learning new communication skills, and as for all things new--*practice*.

Lesson Notes

IT'S TIME TO PLAY!

from *LESS STRESS PRESS*

Remember when your mom said, "*Get outside and play!*" Yes, maybe she just wanted some peace and quiet, but what wonderful direction.

Have you ever wished someone would call you up and tell you to, "*Go outside and play!*" Well, from us to you, "**GO PLAY!**"

How long has it been since you gave yourself permission to go do something just because it's fun? If you can't remember when...it's been too long. If we will look around at nature, we will see that everything is in a delicate balance. When that balance is disturbed, something uncomfortable usually happens. When we do not lead a balanced life, we slowly become uncomfortable.

One of the reasons there are twenty-four hours in a day is because it can be evenly divided by eight, eight hours of work, eight hours of sleep, and eight hours of play. Granted that's pretty ideal, but I'm sure that most of us could do a much better job of balancing our lives if we thought about it a bit.

In case you've forgotten...the benefits of play are many. Play enhances every aspect of our lives. Play necessitates ACTION, it gets our bodies moving, is good for circulation, muscle conditioning, increases our metabolism and helps use up the stress chemicals we may have manufactured during our day. Play gives us the opportunity to interact with others, such an important activity for us "people-people." It helps us get out of ourselves and get into the present moment. Play reminds us to be more spontaneous, something that anxiety disorder sufferers need to practice.

We all know that laughter is good medicine; when we play, we are very likely to laugh. "*Humor has a profound connection with physiological states of the body,*" says Raymond A. Moody, M.D., (We did not make up that name to add humor to this article.) in **Laugh after Laugh: The Healing Power of Humor**. Dr. Moody says, "*Over the years I have encountered a surprising number of instances in which patients have laughed themselves back to health, or at least have used their sense of humor as a very positive and adaptive response to their illnesses.*"

In a recent study they found a correlation between our sense of humor and our I.Q. Sooo, if you want people to think you're smart you'd better start smiling! And while you're doing that...**GO PLAY!**

Best Wishes

Carolyn Dickman
Education Director, Midwest Center for Stress & Anxiety

Do you have questions, concerns or need support? Help is just a phone call away! Call-a-Coach 1-800-515-1133.

6-10

LESSON 7

Assertive Behavior

"Get what you want....self-respect."

Assertive Behavior: Speak Confidently and Gain Respect

OBJECTIVES - Lesson 7:

* To understand the difference between being assertive and being aggressive.

* To understand assertiveness is a learned skill.

* To use assertiveness and decrease anxiety and depression.

* To see that being used and manipulated can't happen without your cooperation.

* To understand that practicing new skills does produce initial anxiety. Practice also brings proficiency.

Being assertive is standing up for yourself.

It is learning to put you first - learning to express your feelings and opinions. It is learning to say "no." Being assertive is making a statement about how you feel about a subject or situation.

By being assertive, you stand less of a chance of being victimized, manipulated or made to feel guilty and used.

Some feel that by being assertive, people will see them as selfish, unkind and inconsiderate. People who suffer from chronic anxiety are so concerned about keeping the approval of others that often they will go out of their way not to be assertive. They are afraid of disapproval, which would bring about self-hate.

Being assertive is healthy. Being abused and used is unhealthy. If you experience both, you will find the first is much more emotionally satisfying.

People who suffer from this condition are often taken advantage of by others. You are so easily hurt and made to feel guilty that others use this to get what they want from you. In other words, they know what buttons to push to get to you and make you feel bad. If they push those buttons hard enough, they will get the reaction they are looking for.

You must learn to turn those buttons off. You must learn to recognize your weaknesses and learn how to overcome them.

If people take advantage of you, it is because **you *let* them**. You can learn how to stop them.

This is not being selfish. It is simply taking care of yourself. In the long run, your attitude will be better, you will feel better about yourself and you will be there for someone when you want to be - not out of guilt feelings.

Overcoming a lack of assertiveness will improve your life and will help build better relationships.

Being assertive means you value yourself as a person. It means your time and your emotional comfort are important to you. It means you respect yourself enough to fight for yourself. If you don't, *who else will?*

Do you have questions, concerns or need support? Help is just a phone call away! Call-a-Coach 1-800-515-1133.

7-2

Self-Evaluation Inventory

Using the following scale, please indicate the degree of discomfort you would have in the situations listed below.

> 1 - comfortable
> 2 - a little uncomfortable
> 3 - moderately uncomfortable
> 4 - very uncomfortable
> 5 - extremely uncomfortable

- Confront a fellow co-worker about a problem you have with him or her. _____
- Ask a friend for the money he or she owes you. _____
- Apologize when you are at fault. _____
- Start up a conversation with a stranger in a strange place. _____
- Turn down a relative's request for a favor. _____
- Turn off a talkative friend. _____
- Tell a friend he or she did something that offended you. _____
- Ask someone out socially for a second time after he or she turned you down the first time. _____
- Admit you don't know the meaning of a word when you are among a group of friends who ask you the definition. _____
- Tell someone you don't like them. _____
- Accept a compliment. _____
- Argue your opinion when it differs from someone you feel intimidated by. _____
- Return your food at a restaurant when it is unsatisfactory. _____
- Request the return of something a friend borrowed. _____
- Tell your boss when you feel he or she is not doing his or her job properly. _____
- Tell your boss when you feel you have been treated unfairly. _____
- Turn in a dishonest co-worker. _____
- Ask your partner for attention and affection. _____
- Ask someone to put his or her cigarette out. _____
- Look someone in the eye when you are criticizing him or her. _____
- Tell your partner you feel jealous or insecure. _____
- Admit your fears. _____
- Tell others about your accomplishments. _____
- Discuss with someone his or her criticism of you. _____
- Go above and beyond your immediate supervisor if you feel it is necessary. _____

Self-Evaluation Inventory *Scoring...*

25 - 30   Assertive-Aggressive

You are probably quite aggressive. You are not afraid to ask for what you want and you don't have a problem confronting someone. This is good as long as you don't hurt others due to your insensitivity and you aren't pushy or otherwise offensive. Think about it.

31 - 50   Assertive

This is a fairly healthy score. You probably have no trouble being assertive. But at certain times in certain situations, you can be sensitive - which is good. You care about people and their feelings, but not to the point of being abused yourself.

51 - 75   Passive-Assertive

You are probably the type of person who would rather not send your meal back at a restaurant, but you might tell the waitress at the end of the meal - by the look on your face - that the food was not great. You are assertive when you are forced to be or when your among people you feel comfortable with. You could stand up for yourself a little more.

76 - 100   Passive

You probably have a hard time being assertive most of the time. Being assertive gives you anxiety. You don't want people to think poorly of you. This is something you definitely need to work on. Start saying, *"No, I'm sorry I can't,"* a little more often.

101 - 125   Wimp

All right. It is time to start standing up for yourself. You will like yourself better and others will respect you for it. No, they won't stop loving you.

Do you have questions, concerns or need support? Help is just a phone call away! Call-a-Coach 1-800-515-1133.

7-4

Your Assertive Rights

Wrong: When someone close to you needs a favor, it is selfish of you to put your own needs first.

Right: **You should take care of yourself first, if possible, so you will feel more like giving to others.**

Wrong: You should never argue your opinion. It will make others think you are pushy and argumentative. Besides, they are probably right anyway.

Right: **You have every right to voice your opinion and it is just as valuable as anyone else's. People will respect you more for having an opinion.**

Wrong: You should try hard to never make a mistake.

Right: **No one is perfect - mistakes are a part of life. Accept them and go on. Try to learn from them.**

Wrong: If you can't be there for someone or you want to get out of doing something, you should always give them an explanation of why you don't want to do it.

Right: **In most cases, you don't owe anyone an explanation for your decisions. A simple, *"No, I really can't,"* is sufficient.**

Wrong: You should not protest if you feel you have been treated unfairly. Others will think poorly of you.

Right: **You should stand up for yourself if you think you are being taken advantage of. If you don't, who else will?**

Wrong: You should not express your anger to people who offend you. They will think you aren't the nice person they thought you were.

Right: **You have the right to express anger. These people will think twice before offending you again if you let them know you won't stand for it.**

Wrong: You should make an effort to be friendly and sociable, even when you don't feel like it. It's better to act than to be antisocial.

Right: **Everyone isn't friendly and sociable all the time. Sometimes you just don't feel like socializing. That is fine.**

Wrong: You should try to keep it to yourself when you feel anxious or insecure. Others might see it as a weakness.

Right: **Everyone feels anxious and insecure at some time. Often, it makes you feel better to share your feelings and it makes others feel closer to you to know that you feel comfortable enough with them to show that side of you.**

Wrong: You should listen to the advice of authority figures and not argue. They probably know what is best.

Right: **Just because someone is in a position of authority doesn't make them right. You should weigh all the information and learn to trust your own decisions.**

Wrong: If you don't understand something, you should just keep making an effort to understand without asking too many questions. If you admit ignorance about something, people will think you're stupid.

Right: **You have a right to question things you don't understand. That is the only way you will learn.**

Wrong: If you are complimented, you should try to make light of it and ignore it. People might think you are arrogant.

Right: **You have a right to enjoy praise and approval. It should make you feel good, not guilty. Simply say, *"Thank-you."***

Wrong: When it comes to family members, you should really put their needs first when it comes to holidays and special events. Otherwise, they might think you are being selfish.

Right: **You have a right to choose not to be with someone at a certain time, especially if it is going to make you feel resentful. Remember, you will enjoy it more when you are going out of choice, instead of guilt. Also, you do not owe them a lengthy explanation of why you have made your decision.**

Wrong: You should make a sincere effort to be liked by everyone.

Right: **No matter how hard you try, everyone is not going to like you. You shouldn't have to work that hard at being liked or making friends. It should be a natural process.**

Wrong: If someone is complaining and being negative around you, you should listen and be compassionate. Let them cry on your shoulder.

Right: **If they are not doing anything to change their situation, you have a right to tell them you don't want to hear it anymore. Misery loves company, and if they can bring you down - they will. Don't let them.**

Do you have questions, concerns or need support? Help is just a phone call away! Call-a-Coach 1-800-515-1133.

7-6

Name _____

List two present situations in your life where you feel you need to be more assertive.

1. _____

   _____

   _____

2. _____

   _____

   _____

How could you be more assertive in these situations?

1. _____

   _____

   _____

2. _____

   _____

   _____

What is the worst reaction that could come from your being assertive?

1. _____

   _____

   _____

2. _____

   _____

   _____

Name _____

List below any negative thoughts or statements you've had this past week. After you have written the negative statement, replace it with a positive statement on the next line. A space is provided below for the instructor to provide you with an example of a positive statement.

Neg. _____

Pos. _____

Ins. _____

Neg. _____

Pos. _____

Ins. _____

Neg. _____

Pos. _____

Ins. _____

Neg. _____

Pos. _____

Ins. _____

Neg. _____

Pos. _____

Ins. _____

Do you have questions, concerns or need support? Help is just a phone call away! Call-a-Coach 1-800-515-1133.

7-8

Example Homework Responses

Examples of situations where someone needed to be more assertive:

"A friend wants me to do work for him, but I really don't have the time. He also happens to be my doctor."

> **"This is difficult because he has seen me when I didn't have an appointment. He seems to really care about me and takes time for me. I feel I owe him a favor. I could do the work for him at a later date and explain that I am too busy to do it now. I have done him a few favors in the past. The worst thing that would happen is he would feel he can't count on me. Possibly, he would not treat me well as a patient. If he feels he can't count on me, that is his problem. I really don't think it would bother him as much as it is bothering me."**

"I need to be more assertive on my job. I have too much work to do and I never seem to get caught up. I go home tired and resentful."

> **"I could talk to my bosses and explain the situation. I could ask them for some ideas and input about priority. The reaction would probably be positive. They would probably do something to help me feel more organized."**

"My brother owes me money that I know he could pay back at this time."

> **"My brother has mentioned the money in the past, but I knew he didn't have it so I said I didn't need it. I do need it now. I will just tell him I would appreciate the money back. I need it. The worst that can happen is he can say he doesn't have it. At least he will know where I stand and I stand a better chance of getting the money returned."**

"I feel my good friend manipulates me. She tries to make me feel guilty if I don't visit her when I am in town."

> **"I can finally see that this is her problem. I don't owe her an explanation of why I don't always see her. I will see her when I want to and she will have to accept that."**

Remember when you practice being assertive, you need to watch your body language.

Stand erect. Maintain good eye contact. Do not yell or scream. Keep a controlled voice tone. Know exactly what you want to say and why you want to say it.

It is best to think before you react and respond, as you should with anger as well. People who are masters in the art of assertive behavior understand the power of maintaining emotional control. You will be much more effective and seem much more confident in your opinion.

Instead of saying, *"You make me angry,"* you need to use *"I"* statements, such as, *"I feel angry because of what you have said."*

There is a big difference between assertive behavior and aggressive behavior. Aggressive behavior is usually more hostile in nature. Very often, aggressive behavior has a pushy overtone.

Do not be afraid to be assertive. Some people are afraid to assert themselves. It seems they are afraid people won't like them if they change in this way. People who are not comfortable with standing up for themselves may experience anticipatory anxiety at the mere thought of being assertive with someone.

Ask yourself who it is you feel most comfortable being assertive with and why? Then ask yourself, who it is you feel most *uncomfortable* being assertive with and why? If you put this into perspective it may help you realize people you are assertive with, be it your children, your spouse, employer etc..., still love and respect you when you show this side of your personality.

If you don't feel comfortable being assertive with anyone, you need to work on assertive skills. Not being able to stand up for yourself is one of the reasons you have episodes of anxiety.

Do you have questions, concerns or need support? Help is just a phone call away! Call-a-Coach 1-800-515-1133.

7-10

Assertive Behavior

"If a person continues to see only giants, it means he is still looking at the world through the eyes of a child."

- Anais Nin

Depression

Not standing up for yourself, feeling misunderstood and unrecognized leads to feeling small. This can be very depressing. This kind of depression can be traced to a "cause" as in, cause and effect.

You have more control of this than you think! You can't have a feeling without a thought first. How you think contributes to feelings of depression.

If your inner litany goes something like:

"I'm a failure...Everything happens to me...Nobody loves me...Nobody respects me...She must think I'm so stupid...I hate myself."

Why do you expect to feel well?!

You have been practicing positive, compassionate inner dialogue for a few weeks. By now, you realize that the direct opposite dialogue is also distorted:

"Everyone listens to me...The world owes me...I don't need anybody...Nobody gets to me...I am happy all the time."

Cognitive psychiatrist, Dr. Aaron Beck outlines some common global judgements used by depressed self-abusers:

- predisposition to think poorly of yourself. You are always ready to blame yourself for whatever goes wrong.

- tendency to exaggerate problems. Everything is a catastrophe and it happened a "million times."

- egocentric view of life events. *"Everything happens to me...Well yes, but when that happened to me, it was worse."* This is victim thinking.

- belief that life is either one way or the other. This attitude is so limiting. This is a mis-belief. We usually have many choices.

▸ view of oneself as helpless or vulnerable. Victim thinking and learned helplessness, is negative and depressing. When we are in the habit of thinking this way, we feel things are out of our control...something, someone else, is in control of our lives.

You can change! The way we think is also a habit, just like all other behaviors. Non-assertive, depressing thoughts can be countered with the following strategies:

> ◗ **Be prepared.** You know what situations and individuals trigger depression from non-assertive behavior. Create three to five short sentences that are empowering. Commit them to memory and repeat before, during and after an encounter.

> ◗ **Pause.** Notice when you have a string of negative, depressing thoughts. We get to "feel" all of our thoughts. If you don't feel good, check your thinking. Stop the parade! Redirect your thoughts; you don't have to chase down every scenario.

> ◗ **Positive inner dialogue.** Be assertive with yourself! Be compassionate, kind and action oriented. Taking action, no matter how minor, always makes us feel better.

> ◗ **Putdown protection.** If you truly are in the wrong - own up and apologize. Do NOT mentally whip yourself for an hour, a day, a year. Offer to help make things right.

Bait and switch compliments like, *"That color looks great on you, and boy do you need color today."* If you know it is not meant as good natured joshing, ask for clarification. This is a great way of making someone responsible for what they have said.

Asking for clarification can be used to get information about a look or a sound. *"Would you care to share the reason for that, "hur-umph?"* Remember assertiveness is not about winning, but about being heard. When your feelings truly hurt--say so.

Acknowledge when **you** hurt your feelings and resolve not to allow self-abuse.

Do you have questions, concerns or need support? Help is just a phone call away! Call-a-Coach 1-800-515-1133.

7-12

▶ **No more "worstisizing."** *"The problem with you people* (the anxious depressives) *is you always start at the cemetery and work backwards."* -husband of program participant. We imagine the worst when we contemplate being assertive. *"They'll never speak to me again...They'll think I'm selfish...I'll die if...I'll go crazy if..."* Never tell yourself another lie!

▶ **Recognize automatic thoughts.** We all have knee-jerk thoughts. What names do you call yourself? When you perceive that you have made a mistake, what do you say? Notice. Change your semi-automatic thoughts and reactions to respectful dialogue. Would you allow anyone else to talk to you the way **you** talk to you?

Put your assertive foot down with yourself and others. You are a good and worthy person. You must begin to treat yourself as you would a most beloved friend. You are just as important as any other human being. These are very important concepts.

Thought for the week:

An attitude of perfectionism is doomed to failure. Perfectionism is a set-up for stress, anxiety and depression because it is an unrealistic expectation which leads to disappointment.

Action Assignments (do as many as you can)

1. Do "the basics."

2. Use your relaxation tape at least once a day-more if you like.

3. Complete all homework and action assignments in session 7.

4. Practice not "winning" every discussion this week. When it **really** doesn't matter just say with sincerity, *"You might be right."* Note in your journal how this feels. Note also any resistance to this assignment.

5. Put yourself first at **least** once a day. Note how this feels.

6. Use *"I"* statements this week.

7. Practice pausing, saying what you mean, meaning what you say and then drop it and listen.

8. Choose to turn anger off; it cannot co-exist with assertive behavior.

9. Let the important people in your life know that you are making some changes in how you respond to certain situations. *"Some of my old habits were not making me happy. I've decided to change some of them. I will be trying to express my feelings more clearly."*

10. Once per day do the following:

    Level of anxiety overall, for the day:____(1-10, 1=low)
    Level of anxiety after assertive behavior:___ (1-10)
    Level of down feelings when you avoided being assertive:___
    Level of down feelings when you practiced being assertive:___

Briefly note what you learned from evaluating the above.

Do you have questions, concerns or need support? Help is just a phone call away! Call-a-Coach 1-800-515-1133.

7-14

Action Assignments cont...

11.   Review session four at least once this week. What correlations do you see between Lesson 7 and 4.

12.   Practice runs are very helpful. List a few statements that you may hear this week. *"Hey, gained a little weight?"* *"I never allowed my babies to have pacifiers."* Record your responses into a tape recorder. As you play them back listen for defensiveness, aggressiveness, victim-voice and whining.

13.   Look for people who seem to use assertiveness like a fluent language. Listen and learn from them.

14.   Purposefully seek out situations where you will be able to practice being assertive.

15.   Exercise every day. Log the miles and minutes in your journal.

16.   Keep journaling.

17.   Write down your goal this week.

Final Comments

When you master the art of assertive communication you are on your way to real self-control, real feelings of self-worth. When you can say, "No" without feeling guilty, when you can voice your opinion with control and confidence, you will eliminate much of your anxiety. At the core of assertive behavior is healthy self-esteem and self-respect.

If you don't stand up for yourself, who will?

"I DON'T HAVE TIME!"

from *LESS STRESS PRESS*

How many times I have heard that! *"I don't have time to: exercise, eat right, use my relaxation tape, write in my journal, to slow down, to cultivate simplicity...."*

I'm sure most of you have heard the comedy routine that begins: *"You might be a red-neck if...."* Last summer my family was over during a fabulous electrical storm and we lost power. We looked at each other with that expression on our faces that says, *"There's nothing to do!"*

My son picked up his baby daughter and took her out to the garage to watch the spectacular lightening. It wasn't long before we all followed. We all grabbed chairs and sat oohing and ahhing, pointing and applauding nature's beautiful display. (This can be used in mental re-structuring if you are one of many who are afraid of storms. I can't help but think our granddaughter was getting a healthy life-lesson.)

This went on for about ten minutes when from the back of the crowd (and it is a crowd when the Dickman family is all in one place), our daughter Melissa, resident comedian, yelled, *"you might be a red-neck if your whole family sits in the garage and watches lightening for entertainment."*

We might be red-necks, <u>or</u> we might have learned along the way how to get simple. If I've learned anything from my after-Attacking Anxiety-growth period, I've learned it is the simple things that count. Slow down. Take time. Make time.

You don't have time to exercise? I say we don't have time not to! Where are our priorities? Dr. Fisher says, *"Exercise is as important as brushing our teeth."* *It's too bad we don't start to smell bad when we <u>don't</u> exercise, maybe we'd be more motivated."* You don't have time to eat right? If you have time to eat, you have time to eat right. If you don't have time to eat, you are way too busy. You don't have time to use your relaxation tape? Where is the balance every life needs? I wonder why you don't feel well?

You don't have time? As Lucinda is fond of saying, *"We all have the same amount of time. What matters is how we use it."* It really is quite simple. Let's get simple.

Making the time,

Carolyn

Do you have questions, concerns or need support? Help is just a phone call away! Call-a-Coach 1-800-515-1133.

7-16

FOUR HANDRAILS TO HAPPINESS

from *LESS STRESS PRESS*

By Carolyn Dickman

SELF-ESTEEM: a good self-image is protection against anxiety and depression. If we believe we are basically good and worthy individuals, we can get through most personal challenges. Happy people <u>like</u> themselves. How about you?

PERSONAL CONTROL: people who feel that they have some control over what happens in their lives and a plan as to how they will respond, are two-times as likely to be happy as the average America.

OPTIMISM: in general, people get what they look for. While being very realistic and practical, search for the best outcome of whatever your situation. Visualize - believe.

FRATERNIZE: Hang out with friendly people. Outgoing people have a much more satisfying life than introverts. If you find that you have not acquired social skills, watch how others do it. Learn from sincere, friendly people.

If need be, "fake it 'till you make it." There are plenty of studies that show a correlation between how we act and how we feel. People who frown on purpose soon elicit feelings of anger or sorrow. Others who purposefully smile, despite feeling none too smiley, report the beginning feelings of lightheartedness.

This type of behavioral experiments have been tried with self-esteem also, with similar results. So, one way to begin your journey to happiness is to act happy.

Lesson Notes

LESSON 8

Anticipatory Anxiety

"I Am Limited Only By What I Think"

Put an End to "What-if" Thinking

OBJECTIVES - Lesson 8:

*   To understand that "what if" thinking creates fear, anxiety and sadness.

*   To understand that "what if" rarely happens.

*   To understand that the antidote to "what if" is present moment living and realistic positive inner dialogue.

*   To understand that limitations must be addressed with a written plan and action.

*   To realize the value of small, slow, steady steps through the process of change.

By now you should be working on overcoming some of your personal limitations.

The one thing most likely to hold you back is anticipatory anxiety.

Anticipatory anxiety is that anxiety which is experienced with the initial thought and anticipation of doing something.

For example, assume one of your limitations is driving. You know you should be working on this. You know that means getting in the car and actually beginning to drive. You sit at home and try to get the courage to go out and actually drive. You begin to feel anxious. You begin to have "what-if" thoughts such as, *"What if I have a panic attack? What if I lose control and have an accident? What if I pass out?"*

You are anticipating what *might* happen. You are anticipating the situation and anticipating negative, scary results. Consequently, you are experiencing tremendous anxiety before you even get started. Often this is simply a memory reaction.

> **Example.** *"I had my first panic attack in the car. It will happen again. I will lose control. I felt like I was going to pass out. I know I will feel this way again."*
>
> *"I had a panic attack in the mall before I had to leave. What if it happens again? I couldn't do it before, what if I really can't do it now?"*

The truth about anticipatory anxiety is that the actual situation is usually never as bad or as anxiety producing as the anticipatory anxiety.

Your fears are much worse when you are anticipating the situation than they will be when you actually are in the situation.

The wall of anticipatory anxiety is often what keeps you from moving ahead, keeps you from making decisions and following through, keeps you depressed and keeps you from taking chances that will help improve your life.

Do you have questions, concerns or need support? Help is just a phone call away! Call-a-Coach 1-800-515-1133.

8-2

Overcoming Limitations

When you are ready to work on your personal limitations, following these basic guidelines will give you the best opportunity for success.

✗ Try to practice your particular limitation on a day when you are feeling rested and positive. Do not go out to practice shopping, for example, on a day when you are feeling ill or particularly anxious.

✗ If one of your limitations is going someplace - the mall, a restaurant, the grocery store, church - start out by going to the place on a "slow day" during a "slow time of the day." This way, you have a better chance of avoiding the crowd which might make you feel more anxious. If you are going shopping, buy just a few things the first time out. Don't try to do all your shopping for the week. You can eventually work yourself up to longer sessions. In church or a restaurant, give yourself permission to sit in the back or close to the door for the first time or two out.

✗ If one of your limitations is driving, go out on a Sunday morning and drive on a street that doesn't get much traffic. Work your way up to the busier streets.

✗ If one of your limitations is getting together with friends and socializing, set up the situation so you can leave if and when you want to. Tell your friends you will meet them there, but you might not be able to stay long as you have some errands to run. This gives you control over your coming and going. Chances are, you won't feel so trapped and you will stay longer. Eventually, you will feel comfortable enough that none of this will be necessary. Until then, this is the best method to use to get started.

✗ Don't tell yourself you want to wait until you are certain you are over your problems with anxiety or panic before you try working on certain limitations. That is putting the cart before the horse. You must get out and do these things, experience anxiety and understand that you will survive, that it will not hurt you. This is the way you will begin to get over your anxiety disorder.

✗ Give yourself permission to feel anxious while you are out working on a new limitation. *Of course you feel anxious! You are trying something new and challenging."* Try to view your anxiety as excitement. Many of the body symptoms are the same. And be sure to praise yourself for even the smallest success.

Name _____

List, in the order that they affect you, the limitations and problems you still have as a result of this condition. How are you going to work on these limitations?

1. _____

_____

_____

2. _____

_____

_____

3. _____

_____

_____

4. _____

_____

_____

5. _____

_____

_____

6. _____

_____

_____

Do you have questions, concerns or need support? Help is just a phone call away! Call-a-Coach 1-800-515-1133.

8-4

Example Homework Responses

Here are examples of some limitations people still feel they need to work on at this time in the program. Following each example will be their suggestions about how they might work on these limitations.

○ **driving distances alone**

> *"I will practice going a little further each time. I will play my tapes while I drive. I will investigate the exits to know where they are and where help would be if needed."*

○ **crowded areas**

> *"Don't avoid them. Use positive dialogue. Don't anticipate the worst before the event."*

○ **sitting in a group of people**

> *"I will go to church and allow myself to sit in the back, on the end of the row. I will use my relaxation skills to get through, knowing that if I absolutely need to leave, I can. No big deal. But I know that recovery lies in staying and getting through the panic."*

○ **flying**

> *"I feel this is a little more difficult for me to overcome because I don't fly that often. I will plan some short flights, maybe an hour or so. I will fly from Detroit to Chicago because I have a reason to go there. Then, I will go a bit further. I will take my tapes and a tape player and listen on the flight. I'll take some positive books to read and I'll make conversation with the person I am sitting beside."*

○ **fear of socializing and meeting new people**

> *"I am going to be more compassionate with myself. I don't always have to be the life of the party or have something interesting to say. It is okay to just observe. I will start slowly by going to some events with my wife when she asks, even though my initial feeling is to say no. I have been doing this, and once I go, I have fun."*

Example Homework Responses cont...

○ *"I still find myself worrying too much about what other people are thinking."*

"I will say to myself, 'So what if they are talking about me? It really doesn't matter.' I finally understand that people are going to talk, no matter what."

○ *"I have a fear of doctors, dentists, blood tests, needles."*

"I will go to the doctor and have the tests I need. I will tell the doctor that I am nervous and that I have problems with anxiety. If I need to take a break, go for a walk or get a drink of water, I will excuse myself and go. I will also ask the doctor to explain things to me so I know exactly what is going on and how much longer the process will take."

○ *"I fear shopping malls."*

"I'll go shopping during a slow time when the mall is not as hectic. I will take a friend with me and split up from him or her for a while. If I only go to one store, I will consider it an accomplishment."

○ *"I fear having lunch with a friend and getting anxious."*

"I will ask them to drive also and I'll meet then there. I will pick a restaurant that I feel is close to home and that I feel comfortable with. I will think of an "out" (excuse) so that if I feel a need to leave early I can. If I don't need to use it, I won't. I will order something light and quick."

When you are working on overcoming your limitations, it is best to move slowly. Try driving and shopping when it isn't quite as busy. Put yourself in a position of control whenever possible. Prepare "outs" ahead of time if necessary. Do things spontaneously when you are feeling good. Don't plan too far ahead (anticipatory anxiety). All this will move you that much closer to complete independence.

Do you have questions, concerns or need support? Help is just a phone call away! Call-a-Coach 1-800-515-1133.

8-6

Anticipatory Anxiety

Depression

When we are negative thinkers, anything said after, "What if...." is bad news. *"What if I never get over this depression?"* Answering this with, *"So what if..."* probably doesn't feel too comforting.

Consulting the three R's of thought restructuring (is it realistic, rational, reasonable?) presents a way to form healthy self talk.

> *"This is not a reasonable thought. I look all around me and I see that people recover from depression. I am putting myself in the way of healing. I'm proud of myself. My history tells me I am a very strong person. I am capable of learning new ways of thinking. My **want** is my **way**."*

You can change your mood, your state of mind, your emotional response.

Suggestions: Trace your mood. Exactly what thoughts started this? Were my original thoughts based on solid logic and facts? Perhaps this was a fantasy from the beginning?

Make a gratitude list. (use Lucinda's letter on gratitude-newsletter at end of this chapter)

Exercise, socialize (even if you don't want to).

Go on a treasure hunt - find your sense of humor.

Do something nice for someone - anonymously.

Change your environment. If you are an indoors person, spend most of your day outdoors. Change the time you get up in the morning, to bed at night. Pretend you live in France; what would you be eating for breakfast? Research at the library.

Play environmental sounds (ocean, rain forest, mountain springs...) for most of the day. Rent or purchase a relaxation video. (see your ***LESS STRESS PRESS***)

Emotions often blanket us in layers; the strongest gets the most attention. Depression is a strong emotion. What might be under it? Boredom? Lack of attention from family, friends? Feeling unappreciated? Feeling unfulfilled?

Take personal responsibility for how you feel. *"What am I doing to contribute to or worsen these negative feelings? What can I do to help myself?"*

Become "other" oriented. Depression and stress disorders promote self absorption. Client: *"I hate it that all I think about is myself."* Hating oneself is certainly not going to make one feel soothed.

If we were to drop an anvil on our big toe, you better believe we would be fixated on that toe. Our whole being would be thinking, *TOE!* Let's be gentle with ourselves. Depression hurts.

Giving ourselves permission to float with depressed feelings does not mean we need to remain inactive. Look up, see the people around you and listen. What's going on in their lives? What are they struggling with? Can you help? Remember, most people don't want advice - they want someone to listen.

Being limited, having created boundaries, can be very disheartening. Use this as motivation. To change the depression means I must push at my limitations a little. Use what you have learned this week to begin.

Patience! We were not one of the lucky ones to have patience as a personality trait. However, we can practice it and therefore develop it as a part of our personhood. We are capable of change.

It takes patience to work through discouragement. One positive about dejection and anxiety, it does give us an opportunity to acquire, through application, the positive attributes that are so life enriching. Use your opportunities!

HOW TO PRACTICE EFFECTIVELY:

- Self-structure opportunities. You really are in control.
- Write out your plan. What is your goal today?
- Take your list of coping skills with you. (carry-a-long cards)
- Break your goal into very small pieces. Small steps get you to the same place. Build on success.
- Deal with any body symptoms right away-don't let them build.
- Practice frequently and regularly.
- Accept some anxiety - this is normal. Could it be excitement?
- Accept that some days are more of a struggle than others.
- Beware of perfectionism!

Thought for the week:

DEAL don't DWELL.

Do you have questions, concerns or need support? Help is just a phone call away! Call-a-Coach 1-800-515-1133.

8-8

Action Assignments

1. "The basics": exercise daily, use no stimulants, use your relaxation tape at least once a day, use some other form of relaxation, drink water, check your thought talk, record your insights and experiences this week in your journal.

2. Review each of your avoidances, boundaries and limitations. Write a reasonable plan to work on each of them.

3. Write your goals for desensitization on a calendar. Break large goals into small manageable steps-put these on a calendar that you consult everyday.

4. Use your fear this week as a signal that you are about to avoid. Record these occurrences in your journal and briefly make notations as to how you dealt with the fear.

5. Notice when you are using circular thinking - jump out.

6. Every morning acknowledge your positive voice. Affirm and give it permission to speak loudly and clearly as you move through your day.

7. When you are practicing your limitations, think of the color green, breath slowly ([inhaling]*"green-one thousand, green-two thousand"* [exhaling] *"green-three thousand, green-four thousand, green-five thousand, green-six thousand"*), and release any tense muscles you discover.

8. Practice don't test!

9. Use visualization each day. Visualize yourself going through your limitations quietly, calmly and in control.

10. This week it's not all right to say, *"I'll try."* Instead, *"I will do my best. Whatever I do is wonderful."* There is no room for "buts" this week. *"But I didn't go very far."* You went! You accomplished! Period!

11. Stack the deck in your favor - plan success. If your avoidance is assertive behavior, don't start with the most angry and defensive person in your life.

12. List two goals you wish to make happen in your professional and personal life. Be specific. Write a plan that details how you are going to make these happen. Schedule appointments with people that can help make these happen.

Final Comments

Anticipation can be a positive or a negative experience. We can look forward to something knowing that feelings of anxiety and nervousness are to be expected but the up coming experience could be something wonderful or life changing. Or, we can look ahead with fear and dread which may lead to avoidance and as a result a missed opportunity. Start choosing your "what ifs" carefully. Use them to motivate you. Think of it as: "What if" positive thinking. "What if...you finally get control of your stress, anxiety and depression?"

Lesson Notes

Do you have questions, concerns or need support? Help is just a phone call away! Call-a-Coach 1-800-515-1133.

8-10

BUT....BUT....BUT....BUT....BUT....BUT....BUT

By Carolyn Dickman   from *LESS STRESS PRESS*

Recently I was working with someone on the support line and she was describing some challenges she was going through. She shared that someone had been giving her advice about her personal life and she described the person as follows: *"she's my friend-but...."* I stopped her and asked, *"excuse me, did you say she was a "but-friend"?"*

After a great moment of laughter, we finished our conversation. I'm sure the laugh did more for her than anything I could have said. But it set me to wondering...how many of us have "but-friends?" *"Well, you might think thus and so, but...."* *"...but I don't think you can do it."* *"....but you were never able to before."* *"....but what if you fail."*

I remember when I was a negative thinker - I seemed to draw people of a like mind into my life. I have found that is rather common. I now understand that if that is the case, the opposite is also true - if I am a positive person I will draw positive people into my life.

I am not suggesting that we shuck all our friends that aren't perfect, but I am suggesting that we periodically evaluate relationships/friendships. Is this person bringing the best out in me - I them? Why is this person in my life? [I believe everyone is present in my life for a good reason. What is the lesson?]

If you have a "but-friend," check for destructive qualities. Sometimes it is best to learn and then let go of noxious relationships. You might wish to review lesson number seven before doing so. Then, "butt out, but-friend!"

I wonder how many of us are our <u>own</u> "but-friend?"

As you go through the program *ATTACKING ANXIETY & DEPRESSION,* you will became aware of how important it is to be your own best supporter, advocate, cheerleader - your own best friend. I recently had an opportunity to review that lesson. I have been going back to school for the last five years, taking a class here and there. I have a dream.

As I was reading Lucinda's book, <u>From Panic to Power</u>, somewhere in the middle of the book, I became aware I was building in excuses in case I didn't arrive. *"Well, it's because I took that class that didn't count. My advisor was wrong. I'll save money if I do it this way..."* - you know the dialogue. What a "but-friend" I've been to myself!

I slammed the book shut, grabbed my college catalogue and guess what day it was - the last day to register for the quarter. Talk about providence! Talk about divine messages! Talk about a book that speaks to you! (If you haven't read it yet - do it!)

I've known for a long time that I will have to take a very difficult (according to my University advisor) math class in order to finish my first degree. Dialogue: *"But I'm not good in math. My high school teacher just passed me to get me out of the room. Algebra and geometry kept me off the honor roll. I'm not the kind of thinker it takes to understand math. I'm more of an "arts" person."* I wonder why I had been putting off taking the math class?

I've signed up for college algebra level one. I have my speech ready if anyone asks me what the heck I'm doing in math 117. *"Most people my age would be taking a sky-diving class. But I chose to terrorize myself with a math class.*

I even tried to study for the placement test! I was nervous. *"But, what if someone discovers I'm not really all that intelligent. That'll blow my cover!"*

At some point in time I yelled a big, *"STOP!"* What was I doing? The same kind of behavior as before the program. I was making myself miserable. I was tearing myself down. I was not behaving like a best friend. I changed the dialogue. *"I have not been exposed to math as an adult. I have learned many problem skills since high school. I know how to study. I am not bashful about asking for help. I believe in my ability to study hard."* (By the way, I scored above average - cover still in place).

I took myself back 25-years and looked for affirmations. I reminded myself that when I taught on the elementary level, the subject I passionately loved to teach was math. I knew what it felt like "not to get it." I was determined. If I had to stand on my head, my students would understand the concepts. I was a great math teacher.

Well, I'm two-weeks into my algebra class, first test this coming week. I've discovered many things. I know how to study, much more productively than when I was in college thirty years ago. I am less distracted by nervousness, more disciplined. I am a great "studier." I really do know how to talk to myself in a helpful way.

I have revisited the lesson of: *"You'll learn the lesson - until you learn the lesson."* I have re-evaluated the value of positive, affirming self-talk. I have tuned up my thought-talk. I've had a review of not just algebra! Again, I've proven to myself that the more risks you take, the more you learn about positive living. The more risks, the better it gets. The better you get.

We had another beautiful example of this in group last week. One of the young women had a breakthrough. Her biggest avoidance behavior was being alone. We were on week ten and told her to go ahead and "just do it" while we are all still together. *"Do it while we are here to support you, help you."* Several people in group gave her their phone numbers for the Friday night.

We had also encouraged her for weeks to begin appreciating and loving herself. We assigned the "mirror" exercise. Look in the mirror every morning and say with feeling: *"I love you. You are a good and worthy person. I respect you. I behave with love and respect toward myself."* Obviously, she was also a great student because the following week she reported that she had stayed alone, actually fallen asleep, and hadn't felt the need to call anyone. She ended with, *"The next morning when I looked in the mirror, I almost kissed myself!"*

Love and Kisses to All,

Carolyn

LESSON 9

Guilt and Worry

"Guilt and worry - gifts we give ourselves"

Get Off the Guilt and Worry Treadmill

OBJECTIVES - Lesson 9:

* To see that guilt and worry are behaviors that cause anxiety and depression.

* To understand guilt and worry can be positives if used wisely.

* To use guilt and worry states as "reality checks."

* To practice present moment living.

* To practice shifting from negative guilt and worry behavior to problem solving action mode.

Very often, people who suffer from anxiety and depression spend much of their time dwelling on the past or worrying about the future.

Many harbor a lot of guilt about things that may have happened in the past.

Maybe you feel you did something unforgivable and you deserve to be punished for it. Maybe you feel that's the reason you are suffering so much now. Maybe you feel guilty about something that happened to you when you were a child. Most likely, it's something that wasn't your fault, but you've been carrying the guilt around for years.

Maybe your guilt is over present behavior. You might feel that deep inside you are a mean, selfish, inconsiderate person. You may harbor resentment because of all you do for others and this makes you feel guilty. Maybe you feel you have recently done something bad or wrong. Your particular guilt might have something to do with the way you have been reared or are rearing your children. You might feel guilty about the lack of attention you give your parents. Or, you may feel guilty about the way you treat your spouse.

Wherever your guilt is coming from, it all breaks down to the same self-hate label. *"I am a bad person. I did something wrong. I should be punished."*

Most often, people who continually blame and persecute themselves blow the bad things they have done way out of proportion. You would be willing to forgive someone else for doing something he or she sincerely regretted. Why can't you forgive yourself?

Sure, there are certain things you might have done in the past or present that were not right. Dwelling on them and beating yourself up over and over again will only cause negative, non-productive feelings about yourself. You are trying to change that. You can start learning how to forgive yourself.

Most everyone gets something from feeling guilty. Guilt is a great way to fill the present moment. That way, you don't have to think about changing. By worrying about the past, it's hard to concentrate on the present or future.

Often, when you feel guilty it makes you feel that others will think better of you for feeling the guilt. This is especially true if you feel the wrong you did was to them. By feeling guilty and letting them see it, they know you are paying for what you did.

Do you have questions, concerns or need support? Help is just a phone call away! Call-a-Coach 1-800-515-1133.

9-2

Often, people harbor guilt for many years as a way of paying themselves back for the wrong they did. After all, you deserve to feel bad. For some, feeling bad feels so comfortably familiar that they almost prefer it to feeling good. Feeling good can bring on a tremendous amount of anxiety when you feel you don't deserve to feel good.

Feeling guilty for past wrongs is a great way to explain your present unhappiness and dissatisfaction with yourself and your life. *"I deserve to be unhappy."* This is why so many people who harbor a lot of guilt have a difficult time thinking positive or taking positive steps to improve their life. Somewhere in the back of their minds, they know happiness won't last for them. They don't deserve it. Why even bother to try for happiness. This attitude is extremely self-defeating.

It is very difficult for people who suffer from anxiety and depression to let go of guilt. These people are extremely analytical. They dwell on the bad thing they did - dissecting it over and over, trying desperately to justify their behavior to themselves. But they never quite believe their justification.

Feeling guilty brings on that feeling of self-hate. It justifies your self-hate somehow, and that almost feels right. Of course you don't like yourself. Of course you're depressed. Look what you did!

It's twice as difficult to let go of guilt if someone is blaming you for something they feel you did to them. No one has the right to do that to you. Try to recognize this as their problem.

Letting go of guilt is very difficult. But it is possible and it's extremely freeing.

You start by taking a serious look at what you did. You need to put it into perspective.

Here are some questions to ask yourself:

1.   Did you consciously and deliberately do something just to hurt someone else, or did you do this wrong out of a need you felt you had at the time? Maybe the pain you were experiencing caused you to hurt someone else in the long run.

2.   Was the wrong that happened a total accident on your part? In other words, you never meant for it to happen. It happened due to circumstances and the situation at the time. Many bad things in life just happen and no one is to blame. Was it one of those things?

3.   Was the wrong you did really that terrible, and if so, by whose standards?

4.   Was the wrong you did something you can make up for? Was it something you can correct, change or apologize for?

5.   Was the wrong that happened someone else's doing? Are you feeling guilty for something someone else is really responsible for?

6.   Is the guilt you feel productive or non-productive? Are you beating yourself up and making yourself miserable? Or, are you being realistic, feeling regretful and remorseful for your actions and taking steps to develop a strategy for change, forgiveness and acceptance? If possible, will you make it right, learn and mature from the error and forgive yourself?

It isn't wrong that you should experience a certain amount of regret and remorse for wrong doings. It is a human response.

It is wrong to dwell on wrong doings. This is totally self-defeating and negative thinking on your part. Remember, you *choose* to feel this way. It's your life. It's time you took control of the way you feel and let yourself be happy!

Rules for Letting Go of Guilt

1.   Using the material on the preceding pages, analyze your wrong doing. Make sure you do this maturely, with a realistic, open mind. This may be difficult at first, but like anything else, it gets easier each time you do it.

2.   If your wrong doing is something you can apologize for, do so. It doesn't matter how much time has passed. If you feel you hurt or mistreated someone, find a way to let them know you are sorry. This is extremely important in order for you to let go and move on. You will be amazed at the relief you feel.

3.   Set a time limit on your guilt. How long will you suffer for this mistake? An hour? A day? A year? Hopefully not a year! Take some time alone and think about what you did. Reflect on why it happened. What was the situation at the time? What can you do to make sure it doesn't happen again? What can you learn from it so you can give yourself something positive from the experience? How about credit for growing, learning and becoming more responsible? Doesn't this sound better than beating yourself up and making yourself feel bad? You get absolutely nothing from that - except sickness.

Do you have questions, concerns or need support? Help is just a phone call away! Call-a-Coach 1-800-515-1133.

9-4

Rules for Letting Go of Guilt cont...

4.   Adapt an *"Oh well, I'm human"* attitude. It gives you the freedom to make mistakes, which gives you the freedom to take chances. Everyone makes mistakes. The smart ones forgive themselves, learn from their errors and move on to try again.

5.   *Let go.* Say out loud to yourself, *"I forgive myself for that. It's over and done. I'm not going to waste precious moments by dwelling on the past. Life is too short. I choose to be happy now."* Guilt is just that - a waste of precious time.

Dealing with Worry

Worry is common among people with anxiety and depression.

You tend to worry about everything from what someone thinks of you to what's wrong with your health. Many of you worry about things over which you have no control. This is a waste of time. If you are worrying about things you can control, then start to take control.

Many people who smoke worry about having a heart attack. Yet, they continue to smoke. Others who worry constantly about their health and heart attacks continue to overeat, overwork, drink too much, eat poorly and not exercise. This is a matter of self-control. If you truly want to lessen your worry, decrease your odds of having these problems by taking better care of yourself.

Worrying about the future is simply a negative habit that needs to be broken. You can unlearn this behavior. Ninety-seven percent of the things we worry about never happen. Why waste precious time worrying about the future when chances are quite good that what you are worrying about will never happen?

Maybe you feel your worries are valid. You feel you have a legitimate reason to worry. Maybe you feel your marriage is going poorly and you might end up alone. Maybe someone close to you is dying. Maybe you are worried about serious financial concerns. These are all legitimate concerns. But it does absolutely no good to worry.

If you can't do anything to change that particular problem's outcome, you should be spending your time forming a plan of action for how you will handle the situation, if and when it occurs. If you can do something to change the outcome, take action to change it. This also requires positive planning on your part.

Stop wasting your time and making yourself feel depressed.

If you are worrying about something over which you have no control, you are wasting your time. Maybe you are worrying about how your kids are living their adult lives. This is something you

you have no control over. It does absolutely no good to worry about it. It just wastes your time and makes you anxious. Maybe you worry about your health. This will only make you feel sick. If you are worried about your health, go to a doctor and make sure you are healthy. Then, stop worrying about it.

To help yourself eliminate worry, follow these guidelines:

▸ Put your worries into two-categories - things you have some control over and things you have no control over. Let go of the things you have no control over. For the things you do have control over, form a plan of action that will produce a more positive outcome.

▸ Use the law of averages to try and decide how valid your worries are. What are the odds of this really happening?

▸ Don't waste time thinking about trivial things. In a few days you won't be thinking about it anymore anyway, so why think about it now?

▸ Do the best you feel you can with things and believe that you did the best you could with each situation. If you are worried about how your kids will turn out, do the best you feel you can realistically do to rear them and realize there will come a time when it will be beyond your control.

▸ If you are worried about money, do something as interesting and productive as you can to improve your financial situation. Don't just sit around and complain. Do something! If you are worried about your health, go to a doctor and have a check up. If he says you are healthy, believe him. If you smoke, drink or are overweight, take serious action to eliminate these negative habits.

▸ Analyze what it is you are worried about. What is the cause of concern? What are all the possible alternatives to the problem? Which approach will you take? How can you put your plan into action?

▸ Live more day to day. Don't spend so much time in the future!

▸ If you are worrying about something very real, something that is most certain to happen, something that can't be prevented and will have a negative outcome - prepare yourself mentally for the worst and accept it. Then devote your time and energy to trying to improve the end result for you. What can you do to ease the anxiety of the end result?

▸ Keep active and busy. Worry is usually the result of too much thinking time on your hands.

Do you have questions, concerns or need support? Help is just a phone call away! Call-a-Coach 1-800-515-1133.

9-6

Name _____

What are some of the things you are feeling guilty about, either past or present?

_____

_____

_____

_____

Which of these things can you do something about, possibly change or apologize for? Which of these things can you do nothing about? Which are some of your main concerns or worries at this time?

_____

_____

_____

_____

Are these legitimate (realistic) concerns? Do you have any control over whether or not these things will really happen? What could you do to change the outcome you are worried about to possibly make it turn out better?

_____

_____

_____

_____

Example Homework Responses

What are some of the things you feel guilty about and what can you do about these things?

Examples:

- *I had an affair.*

  I guess I need to let go and forgive myself. I can't change it. I have suffered enough.

- *I didn't live up to my father's expectations.*

  I am going to stop trying to please him. He did the best he could. I am doing the best I can. I need to let go of my resentment for him.

- *I feel like I've been a bad mother as a result of my anxiety. Sometimes I have a bad temper and yell.*

  I know this about myself and I am going to work on it. I also know that I am a good, loving mother. Nobody is perfect. When I was having all my problems with anxiety, I really couldn't help it. I am doing better and I will work on doing a better job of being a good role model and mom.

What are some of your main worries and are they realistic?

Examples:

- *I worry I am not making enough money.*

  I am starting to make financial plans. Also, I am looking at changing careers. I have wanted to do this for a long time.

- *I am worried about my progress in the program.*

  I am doing the best I can and working hard with the materials. I can see some very positive changes and I know this is just the beginning. It took years for me to get this way. I need to give myself time to change.

Do you have questions, concerns or need support? Help is just a phone call away! Call-a-Coach 1-800-515-1133.

9-8

LESSON 9

Guilt and Worry

We have learned over the past eight weeks that our thoughts can either hurt us or help us. We must at this time face the fact that long-term guilt hurts us, and we can't expect to feel peace and happiness when we hold on to guilt.

Wherever we are today is the end result of our past thinking. If we want to change our future, we must change our present thinking.

Guilt is a negative depressive state. Guilt attacks our spirit, mind and body. It devastates self-regard.

"Worry affects circulation, the heart and the glands, the whole nervous system...."

Charles H. Mayo

Worry bombards the mind and saps energy and happiness. It keeps us from joy. Worrying about something that has not happened is living in the land of "what if."

People that suffer with depression have taken worry to its greatest heights. Worry becomes a way of life; it actually feels "normal" to some.

Worry and guilt are very ego based. Worry assumes I have control. Not allowing self-forgiveness puts us above the Master Planner. Think about it.

***Guilt Grenades* for your consideration:**

> ~ Guilt is depressing.
> ~ Guilt is stagnating.
> ~ Guilt keeps us trapped in the past.
> ~ Guilt is anger directed at oneself.
> ~ Guilt is arrogance.
> ~ Guilt is another control issue.
> ~ Guilt allows us to avoid.
> ~ Guilt is an emotional rip-off.

Solution: Learn from the situation. Write about what you learned. Apologize if another person or persons were involved. Forgive yourself! Let go, move on with the new insights you have.

Letting go is action oriented. We are in the habit of sitting with, pondering, prolonging and procrastinating. We have the power, knowledge and capability to change our habits.

*What **action** can I take today with regard to my guilt?*

FOR YOUR CONSIDERATION:

> ~ Worry is depressing.
> ~ Worry is a control issue.
> ~ Worry is imagining life the way you don't want it to happen.
> ~ Worry is wasted effort.
> ~ Worry creates a mental picture that our brain responds to - as if it were real.
> ~ Worry is a choice.
> ~ Worry is in the form of thoughts...thoughts are not necessarily facts.
> ~ Worry is mostly erroneous.
> ~ Worry is not magic.
> ~ Worry is mentally, physically and spiritually exhausting.

Solution: Switch from worry to action.
Be goal oriented.
Question the validity of worry thoughts.
Catch yourself, interrupt and refocus.
Picture life the way you want it to happen.

We are very talented at upsetting ourselves. The way we think has a great deal to do with how we feel. (We can't repeat this often enough.) It's not the "worrisome thought" that is the problem; it's that we "play" with the thought over and over and over. In other words, it's our style of thinking that makes trouble.

Circular thinking, always ending up in the place you started, is not problem solving. Obviously, once is not enough for worriers. We go on to make ourselves miserable about being miserable. Key: Change our "style" of thinking. Become problem solving oriented.

Everyone worries sometimes. When your child is seriously ill, when there is a world crisis, it is understandable if one worries. However, people who suffer with anxiety and depression worry chronically.

Worriers think that worrying will somehow give them a protective coating. They think that if they worry about something long enough they will figure out an answer that protects them from death, the tax man and holes in the ozone layer.

What action can I take today regarding my worry habit?

Do you have questions, concerns or need support? Help is just a phone call away! Call-a-Coach 1-800-515-1133.

9-10

Action Assignments

1. The usual "basic" assignments.

2. Establish a planned worry time. Plan a 20 minute period during the day. Tell yourself all day when worries pop into your head that you will think about that at 3 P.M. (or whenever you have designated as worry time) - then refocus. Write the worry or concern down and during your 20 minutes allow yourself to worry, but start to problem solve as a part of this time frame. Write about your experience in your journal.

3. When guilt creeps into your mind create a mantra of three or four sentences to replace it with. *"I forgive myself. I am a good and loving person. I deserve to be guilt free. My mind is peaceful."*

4. Try not to respond to anyone's attempt to make you feel guilty. Recognize that you have a choice as to how you respond. Begin using your mantra. Note your experience.

5. Practice apologizing. Absolute sincerity and brevity are necessities.

6. Write your first forgiveness list, alone, in your journal, by free flowing water (symbolizes cleansing). Your list will be divided into two parts. One lists the things you need to forgive others for and the other lists the things you feel you need to forgive yourself for.

Your lists must be very specific. For example: *"I forgive John for making a joke at my expense on June 31, 1944."* When finished with your lists, go back through them and see which incidents you are truly ready to let go of. (Reality based thinking is a great help. If you have been holding on to resentment since 1944-the statute of limitations has run out.)

Continue making forgiveness lists every week until you have a blank piece of paper. Some incidents will require the help of a professional, experienced in a specific area (child abuse, rape...).

Forgiveness is a process. Allow the necessary time and be realistic about this.

Action Assignments cont...

7.   Cross examine guilt. There must be sufficient reason to take on the pain of guilt. Always check out the facts. *"Your Honor, I would like to examine the witness! Were your actions or inactions, the cause of the problem? Is this situation due to circumstances beyond your control? Is there a pattern to my guilt? If so, what can I learn about myself, my vulnerabilities, my strengths?"*

It is often helpful to share your experiences of guilt and shame with trusted friends. Doing so can assure you that you are not alone. This can also serve as a reality check for you. Is this something that others would feel guilt over? Is this really MY problem?

8.   Before going to bed each night, write down three of your most bothersome worries from your day. After each one, jot down three things you will do the next day that will lead to a solution. Do this every night for twenty-one days (time needed to form a new habit). Objective: Let's get into the habit of taking action.

9.   On small pieces of paper, write every worry you can think of. Gather your bundle of papers, put them some place private and safe. Count forward on your calendar thirty days, mark with a symbol of your choice. Do not touch these worries for thirty days.

After 30 days retrieve and go through them making two piles, one for worries that have taken care of themselves and one for those that still exist. Objective: Dramatic illustration of how many things take care of themselves.

10.   Take two different days this week and keep track of how many minutes you spend worrying. Write this in your journal. Keep track for three weeks. If you are working on this, you will see a gradual diminishing of time spent.

11.   Catch yourself worrying. Make a fist and release it as you inhale for two seconds and exhale for four seconds. Repeat three times. Re-focus your thoughts on something in the here and now.

12.   Keep a log in your journal about your experiences with all the behavior changing techniques that you find especially helpful to you.

13.   Write down your goal for this week.

Do you have questions, concerns or need support? Help is just a phone call away! Call-a-Coach 1-800-515-1133.

9-12

Lucinda's Letter

from *LESS STRESS PRESS*

Hello Everyone!

Well, this is certainly the time of year to be grateful...yet, so many of us aren't. We tend to focus on the "have nots" in our lives instead of the "haves."

Why are so many of us so dissatisfied with everything...our looks, our accomplishments, our place in life our jobs or careers, our marriages, our mates, our sex lives, our children, our parents, our homes, our hair, our friends, our parenting, our paychecks, our cars, movies, actors, athletes, books...did I leave anything out?

Why can't my husband help me more with the housework and do it right? And will he ever loose those extra 30-pounds? Will I? Will we ever stop working so hard and have more financial security? Will my children ever really enjoy reading or stick to something? Will my wife ever be more sexually motivated? Will my husband ever understand when I feel overwhelmed? Will my older sister ever realize that I am a grown woman with advice to offer her? Will my mother ever stop telling me how to raise my children? Will I be happier when I get that new job, that new house, that new haircut?...Is she happier than me...are they happier than us?

And of course, if we won't let ourselves be happy...right now...wherever we are...we might find happiness and feelings of satisfaction forever eluding us.

So, is anyone really satisfied...happily married...content with their place in life...happy? And the answer is...sometimes. The truth is you have to *carpe deum* - seize the day - the moment. Let yourself be happy in your moment. Let yourself smile, enjoy the morning, enjoy the snow, the rain, the warmth of someone who loves you, embracing you. Enjoy the simplest of things...the taste of a good orange, the smell of pumpkin pies in the oven, how nice it feels when your car's heater finally kicks in! No one is happy all the time. No one has a perfect life or relationship. I think people who are happy most of the time are just good at being grateful for what they have...and good at making the most of small moments.

If you have a hard time being grateful, use the following "gratitude check." It works for my family.

1. Start saying "thank-you" to yourself and others every chance you get.
2. Go to bed every single night counting your blessings. (Just being able to lay your head on the pillow with peace of mind is a blessing).
3. Get up grateful...another day to live, another chance at present moment happiness.
4. Appreciate yourself for what you have accomplished in your life...already!
5. Keep your eyes open for opportunities to be grateful (often being exposed to less fortunate than you makes you appreciate what you have and...the best things in life are free...a good laugh, good health, a brisk walk, sunshine..ah.. how wonderful life is).

I remember taking my kids to the beach one day this summer. There was a nice looking young man about 25-years-old acting rather unusual. He would stand and stare at the water...run toward it flailing his arms wildly, then he'd turn around and run back toward the beach laughing uncontrollable. He was different than us...he was a little less controlled... he was uninhibited...he was mentally challenged.

Finally, my eight-year-old daughter Brittany asked me why he was acting that way. I explained what I thought to be the problem. *"Is he happy Mommy?"* she asked, concerned for him. I said, *"In some ways, Brittany, he's probably happier than many people. He probably doesn't worry about what kind of car he could drive, what people think of him and how he looks. He doesn't worry about money or success...he simply lives and he is enjoying himself here, this moment, at the beach."*

Sometimes, I think this modern world we live in makes us all feel like we might be missing something...the movies, the soaps, the magazine ads. The stores jammed with "stuff" guaranteed to make us, our kids, our family "happier." "Stuff" doesn't make us happy. Living well makes us happy. We make ourselves happy. But again, we have to look for moments to seize - and seize them...we have to be aware of what we do have to be grateful for.

I'm grateful for another year of doing what I do for a living. I'm very grateful for my children and my husband...no they are not perfect and neither am I! I've lost a father, a brother and a sister...but losing them has made me even more grateful for the living...my wonderful mother... and my two brothers Michael and Gary...I am very grateful for my health and my recovery from anxiety disorder. I am grateful for all of you and all the joy you have brought us through your letters and phone calls through the years. My best to you all...and God bless you.

Lesson Notes

LESSON 10

Obsessive, Scary Thoughts

"We are not our thoughts; we are our actions"

How to Stop Obsessive, Scary Thoughts

OBJECTIVES - Lesson 10:

* To understand that obsessive, depressive, scary thoughts are a distraction.

* To determine the real concern behind over-reactive illogical thoughts.

* To acquire, through practice, the ability to defuse the power of your obsessive thoughts.

* To cultivate the insight to use logic and humor while restructuring scary, obsessive thoughts.

* To use "pause" rather than "stop" when dealing with obsessive thinking.

* To recognize thoughts are not necessarily facts.

* To realize that we are not our thoughts. We are our actions.

* To find the themes in your obsessive thoughts and address them.

We revise the program every 6-18 months to give you the most current help and information. **Please note, that the thought replacement dialogue Lucinda refers to on this lesson tape NO LONGER appears on side two of the lesson tape.** Instead, you will find this dialogue printed in your workbook (pg. 10-9). Why? Because we have found a more effective way to accomplish this additional aid.

Choose someone who really cares about you and ask them to record the script (pg. 10-9). Listen to that recording for 21-days. Then, record the *same* script in your own voice, perhaps adding a few points to make it more personal for you. Now, listen to **your** taped version for another 21-days.

Almost everyone who suffers from anxiety and depression has a problem with thinking obsessively.

In other words, we tend to dwell on things.

Many people say it feels like their mind is just racing. Some find they are more prone to this at bedtime. Others find they can obsess about almost any negative situation or thought at any time of the day.

Some of the more common obsessive thoughts would be:

> -hurting yourself or others
> -thoughts of dying
> -going insane
> -losing control of yourself while you are in a situation
> -getting physically sick - having a serious illness
> -something someone said or did
> -thoughts about your anxiety
> -questioning your sexual identity
> -thoughts with a religious theme

Of course, there are others, but these are the most common. Feel free to add yours to the list.

The most important thing to remember about an obsessive thought is that you will not act on it!

When you begin to feel your mind racing about a particular thought, stop and ask yourself - what is really bothering you? What is going on in your life right now that you don't want to deal with because it would make you feel anxious?

Often, the situation you may be avoiding is totally subconscious. You may not be able to pinpoint it. No big deal! Just recognize your obsessive thought for what it is and know that you are not going to act on it.

Do you have questions, concerns or need support? Help is just a phone call away! Call-a-Coach 1-800-515-1133.

10-2

The thought is not the problem; it is the style, the pattern of our thinking that becomes a problem.

Before you can have a feeling, you must have a thought. If we don't like how we are feeling, we must change what we're thinking.

Obsessive, scary thoughts are just another way to avoid. If one gets really busy with circular, irrational, unreasonable, unrealistic thinking, one does not have to deal with whatever started the cycle. Maybe it is questions we have about our relationship. Rather than deal with our doubts and concerns, we begin obsessing about our health.

Obsessive, scary thoughts are also attempts at control. If one dwells in "what if" thinking, and stays with it long enough, maybe we will come up with a way to control every nuance of the "what if." That is one of the rationalizations for chasing down every scary thought. *"I'll chase it down just to see how scary it gets. That way if it really happens, I'll be prepared."*

The obsessive thought does not necessarily have to be scary. It need only be something you can't seem to put away. Whenever you have a "free" moment, you get it out and play with it.

When you find yourself walking in a circle, just jump out.

We can become sensitized to our thoughts. We've all experienced this. What happens when as a small child you touch a burner on the stove? You were immediately conditioned and sensitized. You will not, on purpose, be touching a burner again. This is good.

You can also be sensitized and conditioned to a smell. Think about the smell of cookies baking in the oven. Your mouth may water. You may be able to mentally smell your mom's kitchen after school, even if that was fifty years ago. You respond to a conditioned stimulus. You can demonstrate that a thought, as well as an object, can generate a conditioned response.

Conditioned responses, sensitization, are reversible! It is called extinction. If you don't respond in the same way to a thought, situation, or object, if you choose to respond differently, you will eventually extinguish the previous response.

The process to extinction is called, systematic desensitization. One systematically exposes oneself to a piece of the feared situation, object, thought, over and over. Couple the exposures with a structured list of responses: relax the body, breathe, relax the mind, soothe yourself with truthful dialogue.

HINTS AND HELPS

▸ **Deal don't dwell**! If it's a realistic fear, don't just sit there, get up and do something about what you are scaring yourself about.

▸ **Look for the theme**. If you are day-dreaming about getting in a car accident, maybe the theme is control. What in your life feels out of control?

▸ **Thought stopping doesn't work for obsessive thinking**. There is a very famous study called the "White Bear Study" (see <u>White Bears</u> by Paul Wagner). Participants in the study were told to close their eyes and they were all given a bell. Then they were told, *"Under NO circumstances are you to think of a white bear. If you think of a white bear, you must ring the bell."* Within seconds, the room filled with the sound of bells! From that study, behaviorists concluded that thought stopping does not always work. We find that to be so with obsessive thinking. Thinking, *"don't think of a white bear,"* IS thinking of a white bear.

Solution: Respond in the same way each time you become aware that you are "chasing down a scary thought," just to see how scary it's going to get. First, notice and accept the thought. Second, call upon your relaxation response. Relax from head to toe. (If you have been using your relaxation tape as prescribed, this will take only a few seconds.) Third, breathe. Inhale for two seconds, exhale for four. Fourth, soothe your mind with three or four under-reactive, calm sentences. Gently glide away from catastrophizing, negative, thoughts. The less attention you give to the thought, the sooner it leaves.

▸ **Thought blocking is helpful to some**. Catch yourself at the beginning of thought chasing and use the following visual. *I see in my minds' eye a huge barnyard gate. It swings open. Look at that. The gate is staying open and all those thoughts are stampeding out and down the trail. The trail that leads to nowhere. I know because I've been down that path many times. I do not have to go there again. Now, I am walking up to that gate* (see yourself doing so). *I am slowly pushing* (see yourself do it-feel the effort in your arms and back), *and slowly but surely, I am closing the gate.* (If it is helpful, copy this visual and carry it with you. Read it every time you see that gate open.)

▸ **Write until your hand hurts**. One of the strategies that Reid Wilson and Edna Foa recommend in their collaborated book, <u>STOP! OBSESSING</u>, is to write the scary thought over and over until you become bored with it--desensitized.

Do you have questions, concerns or need support? Help is just a phone call away! Call-a-Coach 1-800-515-1133.

10-4

LESSON 10

Obsessive, Scary Thoughts

▸ **We are not our thoughts**. **We are our actions**. Your thoughts do not represent who you are. What you think about is not as critical as what you tell yourself about what you think.

This week, you are asked to write down one of your scary thoughts and work with it. You are challenged to find some humor in the thought.

After years of working with hundreds of thousands of obsessive thinkers, we know this step is difficult. We know some of you are thinking, *"Difficult?! You mean impossible!"*

Client: *"There is NOTHING funny about my obsessive thought! You tell me what's funny about rehearsing your own funeral every five minutes of every waking hour."*

We have what we believe to be a very good reason for asking you to pursue a humorous replacement scene. Before dismissing this assignment, consider the following:

▸ Fear is one of our most powerful emotions. It is necessary in the grand plan. The greater part of the grand plan is that we survive as a species.

▸ Fear is a gift. Without fear and the chemicals associated with fear, we would not be able to speed away from danger, defend ourselves and our loved ones. Yes, fear is a gift.

Obsessive thinkers are out of balance. Humor will help you balance your emotions.

▸ We propose that <u>humor</u> is the <u>counter part</u> of <u>fear</u> and <u>equally as powerful</u>. As fear creates powerful chemicals that propel us from danger or crisis management mode, so too a humorous thought (mental movie) creates powerful chemicals that sooth and calm our body, mind and spirit. (Review pg. 1-17)

At face value there is nothing funny about rehearsing your own funeral hundreds of times daily. With our either-or thinking, we may interpret this lesson's assignment improperly. We propose: you ARE capable of replacing the grave side scene with a scene that's silly, humorous or just plain entertaining in a lighter mode.

For example: *"Ah, yes, I see my favorite angel is here to lead the dancing, John Travolta! And oh, Gosh - George Burns really is God. And Hallelujah, Bobby McFarren himself is singing at my wake - "Don't worry..., be happy."*

Then carry on. *What are the words to that song - Don't Worry - Be Happy? Where could I find them? The library?.....* Replace. Replace. Replace. As you have practiced calling upon your mind to supply speed chemicals, you now must practice calling upon your mind to supply chemicals that comfort and quiet.

Obsessive, Scary Thoughts

Yes, we know that some have lost their sense of humor, this is not a "funny" condition. But try, this exercise has helped many to find their humor again. It's still there. It just got buried under a bunch of anxiety, fear and sadness.

Assign a section of your journal to scary and obsessive thoughts:
> Write out the bothersome thought: i.e. *"What if I forget how to breathe!?"*

> **Counter the thought**: *"This is an irrational thought. I cannot forget how to breathe. My breathing is automatic. It is programmed into my brain. I will breathe whether I will myself to do so or not. This is just a scary thought. I can under-react to it. I am in control. I know how to handle scary thoughts."*

> **Question and identify**: *"What is really bothering me? Am I feeling smothered by something, someone? Where might I do some stress management? When did I notice my stress level was rising? What happened two weeks ago? Yesterday?"*

> **Problem solve**: Write your plan of action. It might be using the relaxation tape twice a day for two weeks. Maybe you have slacked off in the exercise department. Perhaps you need to initiate a conversation with your spouse, friend, employer. (Decide what you need that person to hear. Make some notes. Review tape seven.)

"What's really bothering me? This **question** *is really bothering me! I keep looking for some buried memory or experience....Help!*

We encourage you to consider that many of our fears are laid down in layers. For example, one might be afraid of driving, but even MORE afraid that once she drives fairly comfortably she will "drive" away from her marriage. Or, the hidden worry may be that once everyone knows she is capable of driving, everyone will EXPECT more of her. When/if you discover another level, address it. Deal with the real fear.

However, if she is obsessing about the fact that she has not driven in ten years, it is obvious that this **is** what's bothering her. Once this has been dealt with, any other "layers" will surface at a later time and can also be dealt with.

It is very helpful to distinguish between rational and irrational fears. Obsessively worrying about forgetting how to breathe is irrational and probably a "cover up" for something else. Obsessive thoughts about an upcoming doctors appointment because she has found a lump in her breast is rational. Don't waste a bunch of time analyzing this. Deal with the fear rationally: take extra special care of yourself, allow normal concern, deflect and replace any fearful thought that you do not know to be fact. Find the answer to your concern as soon as possible.

You may have noticed that built into all the lessons is the opportunity to practice patience. Lesson ten is not an exception. The way we think is a habit. It took years to get good at negative, scary, catastrophizing, futurizing, past"uring" thinking. It is reasonable to expect to devote some time to reformatting our way of thinking.

Name _____

What is your most common obsessive thought?

_____

_____

_____

_____

How often do you obsess about this? When does it seem to come on? (when you are tired - before you go to bed?)

_____

_____

_____

Can you pinpoint what you don't want to deal with that is causing you to think obsessively?

_____

_____

_____

What could you do to face and resolve the problem/issue?

_____

_____

_____

_____

Do you have questions, concerns or need support? Help is just a phone call away! Call-a-Coach 1-800-515-1133.

10-7

Please use the space below to write out an example paragraph of your obsessive thought. Don't worry how bad it may look or if it makes you anxious to write it.

> **Example:** *"What if I go crazy? Could I end up in a mental institution? I couldn't live in a mental institution. Is this the beginning of insanity? Am I going to just flip out and never come back someday? What would happen to my kids and my family? Would anyone still love me?"*

_____

_____

_____

_____

_____

Now, use the space below to turn the paragraph into something humorous about this thought.

> **Example:** *"I'm going to imagine myself going bananas. I'm going to picture myself in a monkey suit running up and down the street kissing people and passing out bananas."*

If your obsessive thought is suicide, you might imagine trying to kill yourself on an overdose of jellybeans.

_____

_____

_____

_____

_____

Read this sheet 10-times a day for the next two weeks, until it bores you. This is important. The idea here is to expose yourself to this thought enough times that it becomes old and non-anxiety producing.

Obsessive Thought Replacement Dialogue

- *I like myself. I am working to improve myself, to be stronger. I like myself for who I am today. I will feel even stronger tomorrow and even stronger in six-months to a year.*

- *There are a lot of good things about me. I am talented. I am loving. I am confident.*

- *I am positive. I radiate good, positive feelings. I am full of life. I love life. I am very glad to be alive.*

- *I am intelligent. I am interested in new things and ready for new challenges.*

- *I have a lot of energy. I am exciting and I enjoy my own company. People enjoy being around me.*

- *I am sincere and honest. I am a real person. I feel good about my weaknesses and strengths. I accept myself for who I am. I am working toward being even better.*

- *I enjoy feelings of excitement. I want to feel life. I enjoy feeling alive.*

- *I deserve to be happy, to feel content. I have a right to go after the things I want in life. I will achieve them.*

- *I am hardworking, enthusiastic and energetic. I am special.*

- *I am a good problem solver. I am confident in my ability to make decisions. There is no problem that I can't conquer. My strength is greater than any problem I might be faced with. Problems are just opportunities to grow.*

- *Lines, traffic, crowds and waiting don't bother me. I don't mind spending time being patient. There really is no emergency.*

- *I can accomplish anything I want. Nothing can stand in my way. I am strong. I am in control of my life.*

- *I feel calm. I have peace of mind. It is good to let my mind clear, to let thoughts drift in and out. I feel relaxed. I feel soothed. I feel comfortable.*

Do you have questions, concerns or need support? Help is just a phone call away! Call-a-Coach 1-800-515-1133.

10-9

Depression

Can there be anything more depressing than thinking about depression? Yes! Obsessing about depression.

The inner thought talk of an obsessive thinker is a race track at times. Round and round the thoughts go - getting nowhere - a mind that can't finish. Obsessive thoughts are repetitive, come to no conclusion and can be very sticky. When you recognize this style of thought behavior, apply the steps that help your jump out of circular, non productive thinking.

~ Notice
~ Accept
~ Breathe 2-4
~ Interrupt - use positive, truthful, soothing inner dialogue
~ Close the gate - visualize
~ Distract - look for the good

Obsessive thoughts about depression are unhealthy when:

The depressive thoughts are repetitive to the extent that everything else we think about turns us back to thoughts about depression. For example a little free fall thinking might sound like this, *"...blue sky, clouds, rain on my parade-again, poor me..."*

The depressive thoughts are by all logical standards- a waste of precious present moment living.

The depressive thoughts are by all logical standards - over-reactive, perfectionistic and victimizing.

Sadness is appropriate at times. The losses that we all experience as we go through life are responded to with, hopefully, appropriate grief. There's a big difference between the sadness over loss and depressive thinking.

Thought talk that generates sadness contains words that are negative absolutes. (i.e. nothing, never...) *"I'll never get over this condition." "Nothing good ever happens to me."* The good news is that with recognition, interruption and restructuring, you can change the set-up-for-sadness.

If you are totally honest, you can see that, *"Nothing good ever happens to me"* is a grossly distorted statement. Besides, why would you expect to be in a mode of action, change, take charge, when this is the message you give your inner self? Anyone would be depressed if they believed, *"Nothing good ever happens to me."*

Obsessive, Scary Thoughts

As you keep track of your thought talk this week, notice any disempowering words you use: *"I can't do anything right."* Inner communications of helplessness and unworthiness take control away from you; the message is "you can't handle this." Thinking in this mode is very depressing. Change the messages!

Be on the lookout for "automatic" negative, depressing thought talk. Over-time, we all develop knee jerk responses to life events. To discover yours keep track on paper of your usual responses to stress and confrontation. Begin to see the **real** message that your mind is receiving.

Every time you feel "down" or "blue," try to rewind your thoughts. What thoughts brought on this depressed mood? Were these thoughts reasonable, realistic and rational? Were the thoughts positive or negative? Were the thoughts courageous and strong? Were they knee jerk thoughts? Would you say them out loud to a beloved child?

Be a pest! Obsessive thinking can go on and on. Use the techniques in this week's lesson to interrupt and refocus any ruminating, negative, obsessive thinking.

Truly depressed people have some common thinking habits:

1. Warping
2. Re-make history.
3. Futurize in the negative.

Sufferers of depression warp all the information that they take in. They are the only one it rains on. They are the only one that always picks the slowest line or lane.

"I should never have been born" is an example of the ultimate history remake. Depressed people see only their "failures." If there is evidence of grand accomplishments, the "historians" will declare that it was "just luck."

"You think this is bad? Just wait until next week." The future, as seen by a depressive, is very dark indeed.

Viktor Frankel was an Austrian psychiatrist imprisoned by the Nazi's during World War II for seven years. In his book: **MAN'S SEARCH FOR MEANING**, Frankel speaks of man's ultimate freedom. The freedom to choose your attitude. Perhaps until your new way of handling anxiety and stress is well practiced, you will experience some depression. Perhaps until your antidepressant is at a therapeutic level, you will experience some depression. We may have to accept some discomfort for a time. But consider please: What possible help can a negative attitude be?

Do you have questions, concerns or need support? Help is just a phone call away! Call-a-Coach 1-800-515-1133.

10-11

Instead of focusing on discouraging, sad thoughts, <u>look</u> for the good. We didn't say <u>see</u> the good but LOOK for it. It's there!

Have you noticed that almost everyone can better their circumstances? No matter how awful something seems, we can make a difference if we choose to be calm, kind, gentle and positive.

It is imperative that you become adept at distinguishing between normal concern and inappropriate nervousness. How you answer your scary thoughts this week gives you an idea as to how your restructuring has progressed. Compare your inner dialogue this week with your homework in session three.

<u>Monitor</u> anxious and/or depressive thoughts and the feelings that are attached to them. <u>Examine</u> automatic thoughts.

Example: *"I'm always wrong. I always fail."*

Self examination: *"Is this statement true?"* Give examples of times that this has not been true. *"Do my examples fit with these automatic, knee jerk thoughts?"* *"What emotion am I feeling?"* *"What body symptoms are present?"*

Purpose: To become aware of the connection between feelings and thoughts. To find viable examples of this fact: we cannot have a feeling without a thought first.

CLOSING COMMENTS

Thoughts, just thoughts, nothing but thoughts. Thoughts are just mental energy. Our interpretation of thoughts makes all the difference in the world. It is essential that we remember that we have a choice about how far we go with a thought.

It is critical that you see the relationship stress plays in an episode of scary thinking. With careful observation you will see that there is a connection between a rising stress level and a rise in racing, scary thoughts. Instead of being frightened, *"Oh, no not this again,"* view it as a signal to do some stress management.

Obsessive, Scary Thoughts

Action Assignments

1.   All the "basics."

2.   Review tape 3.

3.   Buy yourself a gift as a reward for doing so well. Maybe new CD or cassette of music you enjoy. Play your new music as you work on changing your state/mood/attitude.

4.   When you find yourself in an obsessive episode this week, write down your obsessive thoughts and write comforting replacement thoughts on a separate sheet of paper. Throw the negative, obsessive thought sheet away and focus on the positive replacement dialogue.

5.   When you find yourself challenged by obsessive thoughts, take out the gift you purchased for yourself this week. Remind yourself of the dedication and work that earned you this gift.

6.   Be sure to postpone your obsessive worry episodes until your scheduled worry time. Distract yourself physically and mentally and remember that obsessive thoughts are a normal part of the anxiety condition. They won't hurt you and they will go away.

7.   Send thank you cards to everyone who has helped you emotionally in the last two months. *"Thank you for being there for me."*

8.   On two different occasions, allow someone else to do all the talking. Ask questions that encourage the other person to talk. Listen actively: concentrate with eyes, ears and body. By your behavior, the other person will have no doubt that you are totally listening and absorbing what they are saying.

9.   Allow someone else to be "right." Choose a discussion about something that isn't a "big deal" to you. For example: People get "goofy" when there's a full moon. Instead of citing studies that you've read that supposedly prove your opinion, let the other person "win." An example of possible comments, *"Your point of view is very interesting." "You may be right about that." "How did you come to this conclusion?" "It sounds like you are a good observer of human behavior."*

Who are you not to love yourself? You are the lock and you are the key. There are blessings and graces all around you - cooperate.

Do you have questions, concerns or need support? Help is just a phone call away! Call-a-Coach 1-800-515-1133.

10-13

Lucinda's Letter

(from *LESS STRESS PRESS*)

Dear Reader's,

Instead of my usual personal letter, I've decided to answer one of the many, many letters we receive regarding scary, obsessive thoughts, since this is such a frightening symptom for so many.

"Dear Lucinda, My growth spurt started when I kept have obsessive scary thoughts. I have had them before an managed to get past them...Recently...one thought just hit rock bottom for me and for some reason I just cannot seem to let go. I feel so alone and afraid that if I keep going on this way I might just lose my family...

...I have suffered on and off with anxiety, and it is like apart of me. My biggest fear is I don't know what it's like to be normal again since I've been this way for two months now...would I like being normal if I overcame this anxiety? ...I am so confused and feel trapped in my thoughts. I try to think positive thoughts but somehow I seem to always fail. ...have tried medications...so sensitive I get side effects...when I hear someone has something wrong with them, I automatically think I'm the same way. ...some avoidance behaviors...windows closed I think I cannot breathe...sleeplessness...
Sincerely, C.C." (condensed from three pages of ongoing obsessive thoughts)

Dear C.C.,

I have to tell you that your letter was one of those powerful ones that took me back in time to when I was severely anxious and obsessive. Your concern is your obsessive thinking. You are concerned that you will not be comfortable with the new, less anxious you, therefore you subconsciously keep yourself anxious because it is more familiar. You are now obsessing about your obsessive thinking. You mentioned that you watched a woman on TV talk about her anorexia and it scared you. You fear: ending up living with your anxiety because you don't know how to live without it. Then you went on to talk about a friend who suffers with anxiety and you described her feelings and said you hope you don't end up like her.

Let me begin by saying that we are very, very sensitive to other people and their particular problems. I remember reading about people who had various problems with other psychological concerns and it seemed I could relate to _all_ of them. I would read about someone with Manic Depressive Disorder or Multiple Personality Disorder and I would focus on what I read for days, dissecting it, re-thinking it...obsessing about it. I would ruin my day, my week, and fill myself with fear, that is, until I found another scary thought to transfer my energy to, which was usually something about my health or my sanity.

It is important to remember that you are an obsessive, creative thinker and that is not all bad. What is bad, is giving your negative, scary thoughts any power. They only have power if you let them and the only power they have is to make you feel more anxious. Remember most of these thoughts aren't even true! I certainly was not suffering with Personality Disorder and you are not going to keep yourself anxious because it feels more familiar...or you wouldn't have written and asked for help. Your true desire is to find solutions to your style of negative thinking.

Here is a 4 step plan of action to deal with your scary thoughts that worked and still works for me in an obsessive episode:

~Recognize that you are obsessing and that you are probably tired or trying to distract yourself from something else going on in your life.

~Immediately begin to reassure yourself with positive replacement dialogue that you are just over reacting and these thoughts are not realistic. Do not give them any value which gives them no power.

~Get focused on something or someone else. Call a friend and talk about their life. Play with your kids, read a positive book, listen to your tapes, but change your focus - get it away from <u>you</u>. Get out and get involved in the world.

~Go to a spiritual place to find some peace of mind through prayer, meditation and the relaxation tape.

In your letter you mentioned that you tried medication but you didn't like it and that you are so sensitive that you experienced side effects. You must realize that almost everyone feels side effects with these types of medications although they are not always the same. Medications are a wonderful resource for someone who just can't seem to get control of the ruminating, obsessive thoughts. Anti depressants can be extremely helpful in controlling obsessive thoughts. Don't be afraid to consider this alternative if you can't do it on your own. Talk with your doctor. You need to give the medication at least 30 days to see results. I understand your concern about taking medications but I would rather take a medication than feel totally obsessed with scary thoughts. Once you gain control of your thoughts and use the *ATTACKING ANXIETY* skills, you will more than likely be able to go off the medications anyway.

C.C., you are too focused on yourself. You need to do something positive with your creative energy. Write, work, volunteer. Get out and start living life in spite of the thoughts. If you sit there and wait to start living - when the thoughts go away - you are putting the cart before the horse. The thoughts will dissipate when you fill your time and get distracted. If you have time on your hands you will spend it worrying and obsessing, so it is better to get busy.

Finally, remember to stay grateful. This is anxiety, it is not terminal! You can overcome it; I did. But it does take time, patience and constant effort. It does get easier as time goes by. Don't be so hard on yourself. You are not alone, there are millions of people walking this path with you. Stop looking for goblins and monsters and start looking for rainbows and sunshine...They're out there, waiting for you just beyond the clouds. The clouds go away when you "let go" of the scary thoughts and the fear. Just let it go. Trust yourself, trust God. Trust your new skills.

God bless you on your path, Lucinda

Do you have questions, concerns or need support? Help is just a phone call away! Call-a-Coach 1-800-515-1133.

10-15

Lesson Notes

LESSON 11

Medication and Alcohol

"Look for the good in your life"

High Anxiety: The Truth About Medication and Alcohol

OBJECTIVES - Lesson 11:

* To be able to assess your level of depression and dissatisfaction with life.

* To seek appropriate help and guidance when a need is indicated.

* To understand the difference between anti-anxiety medication and antidepressants.

* To gain an understanding of the various types of medications and when they might be appropriate.

* To illuminate some irrational fears and misconceptions about depression.

* To honestly look at your use of alcohol or other substances that mask reality.

There are many questions from participants about whether or not anxiety and depression are genetic. Is it a condition that can be inherited?

It is common for people with anxiety and depression to have parents, grandparents or siblings with anxiety or depression problems.

There is some controversy about the use of medication. Some people respond well to anti-anxiety medications. Some people respond well to antidepressants. Others can't tolerate the side effects.

Regardless, the medication will not change your perfectionist, negative, overly-sensitive personality. Your way of thinking and behaving is what causes the problem.

Medication can be beneficial initially to help the anxious person calm down and function. The concern is that it might give a false sense of security and stifle the motivation to change ones attitude and behavior. If you are taking medication, you must change your attitude and behavior and learn effective coping skills so you can control your fears and anxieties when the time comes to discontinue the medication. And that time will come.

If you are on medication, you must seek the advice of your doctor before you decide to cut down. It is important to decrease your medication gradually.

We believe that if you learn the necessary skills of self-control for your anxiety, you can eventually be medication-free, as long as there are no other medical factors involved. Your doctor will help you with the decision to cut down and discontinue your anti-anxiety medication.

Many people who suffer from anxiety and depression find temporary relief by drinking alcohol. These people are only covering the wound. They are doing nothing to heal it. For most, it is easier to conquer anxiety than it is to conquer alcoholism. If you feel you have a drinking problem, you should contact an alcohol treatment facility immediately as well as consult your physician.

Do you have questions, concerns or need support? Help is just a phone call away! Call-a-Coach 1-800-515-1133.

11-2

Medications used in treating anxiety and depression.

There are many medications used to treat anxiety and depression. What follows is a listing of those more commonly prescribed. For more complete information about a specific medication, consult your physician.

Anti-Anxiety Medications

Most often prescribed are benzodiazepines, which have proven to be quite effective. But there is concern about potential addiction. These drugs generally are prescribed for limited periods of time, in limited dosages, as part of an overall treatment program which hopefully includes some type of coping skills and behavior modification techniques.

Initial side effects might be tiredness, drowsiness and inability to concentrate. Most common are Ativan, Tranxene, Valium and Xanax.

A fairly new medication is Buspirone. It appears to be non-habit forming and has fewer side effects than some of the Benzodiazepines.

Anti-Depressant Medications

Most common are the Tricyclics. These medications can be very helpful to those suffering from depression. The drugs usually are given in gradually increasing dosages until an effect is apparent. It may be necessary for the doctor to try more than one antidepressant to find the one that works best for that individual.

Side effects are quite common with antidepressants. These include: drowsiness, slight dizziness, dry mouth, constipation and change in urination habits. Most side effects, except for dry mouth, should disappear within a few weeks. The most commonly prescribed are Asendin, Elavil, Norpramin, Pamelor, Sinquan and Tofranil.

A fairly new antidepressant, Prozac, is becoming popular as it seems to produce fewer side effects and is helpful in controlling obsessive thoughts.

There are various categories of antidepressants. Only your physician can determine if you are a candidate for medication. He or she also can answer all your questions concerning any type of medication.

Alcohol Inventory

yes   **no**   Do you sometimes drink heavily after a disappointment, a quarrel or when the boss gives you a hard time?

yes   **no**   When you have trouble or feel under pressure, do you drink more heavily than usual?

yes   **no**   Have you noticed that you can handle more liquor than when you first started drinking?

yes   **no**   Do you ever wake up on the "morning after" and discover that you can't remember part of the previous night even though, according to your friends, you did not pass-out?

yes   **no**   When drinking with other people, do you try to have a few extra drinks while the others are not watching?

yes   **no**   Are there certain occasions when you feel uncomfortable if alcohol is not available?

yes   **no**   Have you noticed that when you begin drinking, you are in more of a hurry to have the first drink than you used to be?

yes   **no**   Do you feel a little guilty about your drinking?

yes   **no**   Have you ever felt annoyed by criticism of drinking?

yes   **no**   Have you ever felt the need to cut down on drinking?

yes   **no**   Have you ever taken a morning eye-opener?

If you answered "yes" to two or more of these questions, you may have a drinking problem. The more positive answers, the more severe the problem.

Do you have questions, concerns or need support? Help is just a phone call away! Call-a-Coach 1-800-515-1133.

11-4

Depression Assessment Scale

Name _____   Date _____

Within this assessment tool are 16 groups of statements. In each group, you are to choose the statement that most accurately describes (in general) your present way of thinking or feeling. Read ALL of the statements in a question before making your choice. Please circle only one number per group.

A.   1. I have had no unusual change in appetite.
         2. I have had a mild change in appetite.
         3. I have had a moderate change in appetite.
         4. I have had a severe change in appetite.

B.   1. I am satisfied with my weight.
         2. I am concerned about my weight.
         3. I am not satisfied with my weight.

C.   1. I have had no unusual change in sleep patterns.
         2. I have had a mild change in sleep patterns.
         3. I have had a moderate change in sleep patterns.
         4. I have had a severe change in sleep patterns.

D.   1. I am satisfied with the quality of sleep.
         2. I am concerned about the quality of sleep.
         3. I am not satisfied with the quality of sleep.

E.   1. I have had no unusual change in energy.
         2. I have had a mild change in energy.
         3. I have had a moderate change in energy.
         4. I have had a severe change in energy.

F.   1. I am satisfied with my energy level.
         2. I am concerned about my energy level.
         3. I am not satisfied with my energy level.

G.   1. I have had no unusual change in sexual desire.
         2. I have had a mild change in sexual desire.
         3. I have had a moderate change in sexual desire.
         4. I have had a severe change in sexual desire.

Depression Assessment Scale cont...

H.   1. I am satisfied with my sexual desire.
       2. I am concerned about my sexual desire.
       3. I am not satisfied with my sexual desire.

I.   1. I have had no unusual change in self-perception.
       2. I have had a mild change in self-perception.
       3. I have had a moderate change in self-perception.
       4. I have had a severe change in self-perception.

J.   1. I am satisfied with my self-perception.
       2. I am concerned with my self-perception.
       3. I am not satisfied with my self-perception.

K.   1. I have had no unusual change in my ability to concentrate.
       2. I have had a mild change in my ability to concentrate.
       3. I have had a moderate change in my ability to concentrate.
       4. I have had a severe change in my ability to concentrate.

L.   1. I am satisfied with my ability to concentrate.
       2. I am concerned with my ability to concentrate.
       3. I am not satisfied with my ability to concentrate.

M.   1. I have had no unusual recurrent thoughts of death or suicide.
       2. I have had a mild amount of thoughts of death or suicide.
       3. I have had a moderate amount of thoughts of death or suicide.
       4. I have had a severe amount of thoughts of death or suicide.

N.   1. I am satisfied with the quality of my life.
       2. I am concerned with the quality of my life.
       3. I am not satisfied with the quality of my life.

O.   1. I have had no unusual change in my health.
       2. I have had a mild change in my health.
       3. I have had a moderate change in my health.
       4. I have had no unusual change in my health.

P.   1. I am satisfied with my health.
       2. I am concerned about my health.
       3. I am not satisfied with my health.

Do you have questions, concerns or need support? Help is just a phone call away! Call-a-Coach 1-800-515-1133.

Depression Assessment Scale cont...

Scoring

Questions A, C, E, G, I, K, M, and O demonstrate either physical or psychological symptoms. Add your score for those questions.

       8   absence of depression
    9-16   mild degree of depression
   17-24   moderate degree of depression
   25-32   severe degree of depression

Questions B, D, F, H, J, L, N and P indicate personal satisfaction.

       8   optimal personal satisfaction
    9-16   concern about personal satisfaction
   17-24   lacking in personal satisfaction

DO NOT let your score frighten you. If you feel you scored rather high and this concerns you, please talk with your physician about depression. It is common for people suffering with acute anxiety to be depressed. However, if your score is high, you might feel better talking with your physician.

Example Homework Responses to Lesson 11

If you feel you are someone who may be self-medicating with alcohol, you need to be honest with yourself. You are using the alcohol to take the edge off. The "edge" that you are trying to eliminate is anxiety. If you can learn to like yourself and be more compassionate with yourself, you can learn to live with little or no alcohol.

Many people feel more comfortable in a social setting after they have had a few drinks. The reason for this is that it seems to help you relax and let go of some of your inhibitions. True self-esteem lies in being able to release some of those inhibitions on your own. This will come with learning to change the way you think and respond. When you learn to let go of the importance of other people's opinions, you can relax more socially. No matter what you think or do, you can't be liked by everyone.

The Depression Assessment Scale is a basic assessment of your level of personal happiness and satisfaction. Do not be too analytical about this assessment. When you choose your statement it is suggesting you feel this way in the negative sense. For example:

> *"I have had a mild change in energy."* You would circle the statement only if you noticed your energy decreasing.

> *"I have had a moderate change in my self-perception."* Again, you would circle this statement only of you have had a moderately negative change in your self-perception.

An estimated 70% of those who suffer with anxiety disorder suffer with secondary depression. Don't let this frighten you. This program will provide many skills to aid you in working through your depressed feelings and will help you alleviate them. If at this point in the program you still notice the following symptoms and/or have scored high on the depression assessment, you may want to talk with your doctor about depression.

- feeling tired often
- crying episodes
- headaches
- decrease or increase in appetite
- feelings of hopelessness

- suicidal thoughts
- lack of sexual desire
- lack of motivation
- difficulty sleeping

Do you have questions, concerns or need support? Help is just a phone call away! Call-a-Coach 1-800-515-1133.

11-8

Some Anxiety Induced Causes of Depression:

~ **Personality type:** People who are highly self-critical, very demanding or unusually passive and dependent may be prone to depression.

~ **Environmental influences:** Challenging family, social or working environments can cause depression. Serious interpersonal conflicts, loss of a loved one, neglect as a child, are often triggers for depression.

~ **Biochemical:** Shortages or imbalances of mood influencing chemicals in the brain are thought to play a role in some cases of depression. Be aware that certain medications, illnesses or infections can lead to depression.

~ **Genetic:** The tendency to suffer from some type of depressive illness does seem to run in families.

Some common signs and symptoms:

~ **Changes in behavior:** A general slowing down, neglecting responsibilities and appearance, loss of appetite, and pointless over activity. Poor memory may be noticed, along with an inability to concentrate. Loved ones may notice agitation, irritability, complaints about matters that used to be taken in stride.

~ **Changes in feelings and perception:** Emotional flatness, reporting an "empty" feeling, unable to find pleasure in anything, feelings of hopelessness. Noticing exaggerated self-blame, guilt or loss of self-respect, sometimes leading to suicidal thoughts or actions.

~ **Changes - physical with no organic cause:** Most common complaints are sleeping disturbances, chronic fatigue, lethargy, unexplained headaches, backaches and digestive upsets.

When symptoms are severe and lasting, so that pain and problems outweigh pleasure most of the time, it is time to seek professional help. Please don't try to do this alone.

Client: *"I tried to fix myself for thirty years...I forgot who I was consulting."*

You and your doctor will decide on the treatment that is right for your situation. There are effective medications available that are not habit forming, nor addictive. Do not neglect the consideration of talk therapy coupled with cognitive and behavioral therapy.

Client: After three weeks on antidepressant medication, *"Do you (doctor) mean this is the way everyone else feels EVERY DAY?!"*

Amateur therapy offered by friends, family, etc., while well meaning, should never take the place of professional help for the severely depressed.

The screening in your workbook is meant to alert you that there may be a problem. It is not a diagnostic tool.

Dr. Fisher, M.D.: *"You can't drink alcohol, smoke, eat sugar, guzzle caffeine and expect to feel like God meant for you to feel."*

Get clean and see what we mean!

Do you have questions, concerns or need support? Help is just a phone call away! Call-a-Coach 1-800-515-1133.

11-10

Medication and Alcohol

Action Assignments

1. Do all the "basics."

2. Take the depression evaluation; compare your scores to the scores when you first used this evaluation in Lesson One.

3. Each day this week, go out of your way to talk to someone other than a "safe" person.

4. Each day, walk outside.

5. Rent or go to a funny movie, twice this week.

6. Ask yourself why you feel blue, sad. Problem solve by asking what you can do right that minute to feel better. Decide how you can look at the situation differently.

7. Find a simple need in your family, church, club, work place, community....fill it this week.

8. If you are on medication for anxiety and feel you're ready, this would be a good week to talk with your doctor about cutting down on your medication.

9. If you drink alcohol, make a goal to go a week or two without any alcohol to see how you feel without it. Write about your experience in your journal.

    If you find you are having extreme difficulty eliminating alcohol, marijuana, cocaine...(any other addictive substance), talk with your doctor about support groups, therapies, medications, herbs, anything that will aid you.

10. If depression or your obsessive thinking still seem to be holding you back, this might be a great time to talk to your doctor about an antidepressant.

Client: *"I'm not living...I'm existing...living hurts too much."*

To depressed people, sadness is a way of life. They are often unaware that it doesn't have to be this way. Their outlook is gloomy, cynical and fatalistic (they would call it realistic!).

The depressed are victims of distorted thinking - this can be remedied.

Depression does not have to ruin lives!

"Just wanted to drop another line to say how great I'm doing. It's been seven months since I received the program. I've been studying very hard. I practice all the time and I still listen to my tapes.....I can say that I'm free and it feels wonderful. My life has changed so much, I'm not afraid anymore.

I can actually talk to myself; I hear my thoughts clearly and I can detect any negative thoughts. I can close my eyes and lay on my bed and actually listen to myself, instead of running away from them.

I'm not afraid of my thinking patterns. I have learned so much from this program, it all seems like a dream. I give myself permission to have anxiety, it feels controlled. There have been days that I'm anxious - I use those days to practice. At first, I thought that I would never get better because I still had those feelings. But they are there for a reason. God has created us with wonderful emotions.

Last year I would never have thought it possible to be where I am. I look back on my journals and I read endless cries to God for help. I needed answers; I wanted to know why was I so different. He answered all my prayers...."

L.R. Maine

*"I have been through the Attacking Anxiety tapes, have read several of the suggested reading books and have just two days ago bought Lucinda's **From Panic to Power**, book. It's great.*

I finally have decided to write and tell you my story: I guess I can recall being anxious and panicky as far back in my childhood as age 9. Maybe even earlier, the episodes would come and go and I was never sure of a name or a diagnosis until I was 20. I had just gotten married and when I returned from my honeymoon, my husband and I went into the grocery store and I had a full-blown attack and had to leave the store without getting our groceries. That was the beginning of my nightmare!

I started having a hard time going to work, sleeping, going places, socializing, etc.... Everything was a chore, I dreaded everything. Needless to say, my husband probably thought he had just married a nutcase!

I went through every test imaginable and everything seemed fine - physically (even though I had every body symptom known to man!)....I went to a therapist, a psychiatrist...well, I had the medication, knew my condition, but had <u>no tools</u> to teach me to cope and get over this condition. So, I started going to bookstores and libraries reading up on everything there was on panic and anxiety. I went on like this for about 6 or 7 years, coping as well as I could, going from therapist to therapist, I even tried hypnotherapy!....

*....I saw your **Attacking Anxiety** program on T.V. and probably watched it ten times before I picked up the phone and ordered. That is one of the most positive things I've done in my life. That was in May 1994, I have gone through them twice and value each and every one of those tapes! Also, I love the **Less Stress Press**!*

*....I still have times when I get anxious and still have growth spurts, but know I can't go back now! I'm so grateful for you [Lucinda] and your program [**Attacking Anxiety**], and everyone at the Midwest Center. P.S. I have never written about this before. I hope it will be of some help to someone!!"*

D.E. New Hampshire

We have had several young people go through the *Attacking Anxiety* program. We would like to share the homework notes sent in by a young lady (14). Her insights and focuses will benefit all who are going through the program - **they are as follows:**

When I start to feel anxious-

1. Recognize that it's just my anxiety and it's OK.
2. Accept it, while thinking positively!
3. Don't dwell on how I feel, keep busy and realize there is no real emergency.
4. Do the breathing technique.
5. Know that you always get through it.

She includes the following reminders to herself: realize it'll take time, go through them and become less afraid, eat well, exercise, drink lots of water, vitamins, relaxation tape.

Think of the tapes and the steps to a panic attack. Break it down and know when to interfere, to just stop, accept and relax.

***I wish we all were as focused as this youngster! ***

> *"THE ME I SEE, IS THE ME I'LL BE." The mind is a powerful switchboard from which we get all our direction, and negative, scared thoughts are too expensive to own."* **D.M. AZ (age 80)**

"Dearest Lucinda,

I'm 26 years old and have a two and one-half year old daughter. I finished the program today. There are many things I want to say, but I feel most important is that I love you Lucinda! All that you do, all that you are, you are inspiring to me. When I'm feeling a little down, all I have to do is listen to your voice and I feel so much better!

I could sit here and write what this program has done for me and I would never stop. I truly thank God for your help, dedication and courage. You're quite a woman Lucinda. I hope someday I get a chance to visit the Midwest center and the privilege of meeting you. All my love, **B.S. Wa.**

--P.S. The program is worth a million!"

"Dear Midwest Center,

I want to let you know how good I feel and how good I'm doing. I am now driving again. I also went over a pretty big bridge and instead of a panic attack, I looked at it as a rush of success! It felt great....

These tapes have totally changed my life. I still have a few things to conquer but that's OK I will get there. Look how far I've come and I'm only half way through the program. Lucinda I thank you over and over again.!!!!" **R.S. Ma**

Lesson Notes

Resisting Change

"If I always do what I've always done, I'll always get what I've always gotten."

The Courage to Change

OBJECTIVES - Lesson 12:

*   To understand that all changes cause some discomfort.

*   To acknowledge that every thought, word and action is connected to a "payoff."

*   To recognize your secondary gains.

*   To stop using your anxiety as an excuse for anything.

*   To realize that at this time in recovery, some of our "anxious" feelings are really excitement.

*   To consciously resolve to take personal responsibility for our own healing.

Some of you might be having a hard time changing some of your negative behavior.

For some reason, you just can't seem to give up some of your ways of thinking and acting, even though you know they're causing some of your anxiety and depression.

If you feel this way, let's take a closer look at some common resistance behaviors people use to avoid change. They're hard to recognize in yourself at first. But as we go through this session, be honest with yourself, some of your own resistance behaviors may be keeping you from moving ahead as quickly as you would like. By recognizing them, you will be able to understand the reason behind the negative behavior.

Change in your life, whether it is good or bad, can be very anxiety producing, especially if you're a person who tends to overreact to things. But the only way to let go of this condition is to make changes.

Most people who suffer from anxiety and depression feel they get nothing but misery from having this condition. It just makes them miserable and possibly keeps them from functioning like a normal person. Believe it or not, most people actually get something out of negative behavior such as anxiety.

Some people, subconsciously, would rather remain agoraphobic than give up what they are getting from being anxious, depressed, physically ill, dependent, unable to socialize, etc.

This sounds hard to believe, but it's true. Anxiety and depression are great excuses not to grow up, not to be responsible for your own happiness or lack of it and so on.

Please listen to tape number 12 carefully.

It will only help you move that much faster if you understand what you are getting out of this negative behavior.

The pluses that come from regaining your independence and self-confidence far outweigh what you may be getting from maintaining negative behavior.

Do you have questions, concerns or need support? Help is just a phone call away! Call-a-Coach 1-800-515-1133.

12-2

Common Resistance Behavior

1. **Justifying present behavior:**

    In this resistance pattern, you have a thousand reasons (excuses) for your present behavior. Often, these excuses are weak and are built on a negative foundation.

2. **Negative/skeptical attitude about change:**

    Many people enter the program with this behavior. You may have already decided the program won't work for this or that reason. You may feel the material is too complicated. Or, you're skeptical about cassette tapes.

    This is a self-defeating attitude. You start out by saying it won't work, so you won't be disappointed if it doesn't. This is resistance to change. Unless you try to become more open-minded and try to let go of this thought, you will have a hard time letting go of this condition. You need to recognize that this is simply a resistance pattern. Then, you will be on the road to change.

3. ***"That's the way I am,"*** **attitude:**

    This resistance is usually preceded by statements such as, *"I'm the type of person..."* and so on. It is a statement that says this is the way you are and you probably are not going to change.

4. **Procrastination:**

    This is a very common resistance. You may be saying you will put off working on your limitations until you don't feel anxious or until you feel more independent. You may say that you will go out and drive when the weather is better or you'll be more assertive with your mother when you feel you are over your problems with anxiety and depression. This only keeps you from facing your fears and working toward your goals.

5. **Over-analyzing and intellectualizing:**

    This is a common resistance behavior because, as a rule, you are so analytical. With this resistance, you overanalyze and intellectualize everything until the new behavior seems so complicated and confusing it produces a great amount of anxiety. Consequently, the old behavior seems easier and less complicated. This is your subconscious way to resist.

Common Resistance Behavior cont...

6. **Morals or Religion:**

This resistance is hard to let go of because it is so effective and justifiable. You might feel that you can't put yourself first or be assertive because it will go against your religion. Again, this is simply a resistance to change. It is easier to feel that someone or something else is keeping you in a position where you are being taken advantage of and manipulated. Learning to have respect for yourself and like yourself more is not going against your religion. You must recognize this as one of your resistances to change.

7. ***"Nobody really understands me"* attitude:**

This resistance is kind of a "feel sorry for yourself" attitude. You feel that you are different. Your problems are worse. Maybe you can't change. Again, this is a very self-defeating attitude that will stop you even before you get started. But, at least you have a good excuse not to change.

8. **Insecure behavior:**

This resistance can be effective because it also puts the blame on someone or something else. *"People might not like or love me if I change. Someone might take it wrong if I am assertive. What if I change and my husband or wife leaves me?"* You have all kinds of little insecure reasons for not changing. Maybe it's easier to just stay anxious.

You might feel you are having a hard time adjusting to change. You might also feel a little lost and confused about exactly whom or what you are changing into. That is okay, but you still must change to get over this chronic anxiety.

Changing is very hard. It is anxiety producing. You are probably using some of the resistance patterns mentioned above to keep from changing or to slow the process of change. Even though this condition is unpleasant, it is familiar. New behavior is not.

It is up to you. Which is worse? The anxiety from suffering with anxiety and depression or the anxiety from change? Neither is pleasant, but only one holds the key to self-acceptance, growth, maturity and peace of mind.

Do you have questions, concerns or need support? Help is just a phone call away! Call-a-Coach 1-800-515-1133.

12-4

Name _____

What are some of the resistances to change you find you use now or have used in the past?

_____

_____

_____

_____

_____

Which of these resistances do you feel you might have used or you are now using to resist getting over this condition?

_____

_____

_____

_____

What concerns you most about changing?

_____

_____

_____

_____

Secondary Gains - What do we get out of negative behavior?

▸ **Getting attention:**

This gain is especially important to those people who seem to be "babied" a lot due to their anxiety. The attention usually is given by a spouse or relative who ends up going places with the anxious person, running errands for them and monitoring their condition. Thus, the spouse or relative becomes the anxious person's "safe" person. It isn't easy to give up all that attention, especially if deep down inside it makes you feel loved and cared for.

▸ **Avoiding making decisions:**

This is one of the more popular secondary gains, especially for those who are performance oriented.

Making a decision about your life is very difficult. If you make the wrong decision, you are setting yourself up for self-hate due to your perfectionist, hate-to-fail attitude. By being anxious and depressed, you have an excuse not to make a decision about such things as changing jobs, getting out of a bad relationship, going back to school or starting a weight control program.

What if you did any of these things and your anxiety acted up? Maybe you'd better not do it. Thus, the chance is never taken. You are so busy clouding your mind with, *"What's wrong with me?"* that you don't have time to make decisions. Decision making is very difficult for many anxious people, causing them much anxiety. This will only lead to procrastination, which will result in self-hate. It is a no-win situation.

▸ **Avoiding getting close to people and socializing:**

Getting close to people is a lot of work. Again, this would lead to self-hate. It's easier not to make the effort. Besides, if these people knew what you were really like, they would think you were different and they probably wouldn't like you anyway. Right? Wrong.

If you remain anxious and depressed you can't get close to anyone. They would never understand your condition. The truth is, you can get hurt by getting close to someone. It is a lot of work to maintain a friendship. To some of you, staying anxious is an easier alternative.

Do you have questions, concerns or need support? Help is just a phone call away! Call-a-Coach 1-800-515-1133.

12-6

Secondary Gains cont... - What do we get out of negative behavior?

> **Avoiding doing things you dislike doing:**
>
> Maybe you don't really like to drive. Maybe you hate going shopping or visiting relatives.
>
> By being anxious and feeling depressed, you have an excuse "not to." It can get you out of all kinds of unpleasant chores. And it is very effective.
>
> The problem is that subconsciously, you know you really didn't want to do that particular thing anyway. This leads to underlying feelings of guilt which will lead to self-hate.
>
> You may be feeling bad and guilty and not even understand why. It is okay to not want to do something. But you will feel better when you make a conscious choice about doing it rather that letting your condition make up your mind for you.

You may truly feel you are getting nothing positive out of this condition. If you feel this way, that is fine. But it is important for you to take a serious look at yourself. If you can pinpoint your personal secondary gain, you will understand your condition that much better. You can let go of using this condition as an excuse that much sooner.

Name _____

List below any negative thoughts or statements you've had this past week. After you have written the negative statement, replace it with a positive statement on the next line. A space is provided below for the instructor to provide you with an example of a positive statement.

Neg. _____
Pos. _____
Ins. _____

Neg. _____
Pos. _____
Ins. _____

Neg. _____
Pos. _____
Ins. _____

Neg. _____
Pos. _____
Ins. _____

Neg. _____
Pos. _____
Ins. _____

Neg. _____
Pos. _____
Ins. _____

Neg. _____
Pos. _____
Ins. _____

Neg. _____
Pos. _____
Ins. _____

Neg. _____
Pos. _____
Ins. _____

Do you have questions, concerns or need support? Help is just a phone call away! Call-a-Coach 1-800-515-1133.

12-8

Name _____

What secondary gains do you feel you are getting now or have received in the past?

_____

_____

_____

_____

_____

What feelings did you have when you experienced those gains?

_____

_____

_____

_____

What are some of the activities or situations you would like to get involved in or change if it weren't for your condition holding you back?

_____

_____

_____

_____

_____

Example Homework Responses to Lesson 12

What resistance to change do you use and what concerns you most about changing? For example:

> *"I used them all but a negative, skeptical attitude was my most common."*
> *"This* (program) *won't work for me. It is just tapes. I'll never get better."*

This person said he was afraid to change because it brings about so many symptoms and thoughts of anxiety. Also, if he changes, he is afraid people would expect too much out of him. He said he is also afraid to fail. He is afraid of getting better. What if it doesn't last?

What does he feel he gets out of this behavior?

> *"I avoid making decisions about my life. I don't have to grow up and be responsible for my own happiness. I have an excuse not to socialize. I can stay safe."*

At first, this person had a difficult time understanding this session. He didn't feel he was getting anything out of this horrible problem. After listening to the tape and talking with a peer person, he said a light bulb went on. He felt this helped him tremendously to understand his problems and to move out of a "stuck point."

> *"Procrastination is my biggie. I tend to think, 'I'll wait until...' I also overanalyze. I think of all the reasons why I shouldn't change. I came into the program thinking I had all the answers. I had read all the books. I had already decided this wouldn't teach me anything new."*

> *"I guess my big fear is what if my family doesn't like me once I've changed? What if they think I am selfish? I am a people pleaser. It would make me too anxious. I need them."*

What does she feel she gets out of this behavior?

> *"I definitely get attention. My husband does my errands for me. I also avoid making decisions. It is my excuse not to change careers. It is my excuse not to be more assertive with people in my life who I feel take advantage of me. It is almost like it's easier to stay this way than to risk the anxiety of making someone mad."*

What are you getting out of your negative behavior? Take a risk... Change! Get your freedom back!

Do you have questions, concerns or need support? Help is just a phone call away! Call-a-Coach 1-800-515-1133.

12-10

Resisting Change

Change is the **only** constant in our lives. But, oh, how we resist it. If there were a change resistance scale, people with stress, anxiety and depression would find themselves on the very high end.

We are all creatures of habit. Everything is habit, the way we behave, the way we think, what we allow in our lives. Some of us are in the habit of allowing others to run our lives. Some of us are even in the "habit" of abusive relationships.

When people like us think about change, our all or nothing style of thinking is usually present. We are the instant potatoes people, fix everything in thirty minutes, better yet--fix it yesterday.

In all honesty, we know this attitude isn't reasonable. Life changes take time; they are a process. It took years to get where you were twelve weeks ago, and although it won't take as long to change, you must allow for the re-programming involved in changing life-long thinking and behaving habits.

POSITIVE DIALOGUE FOR CHANGE:

Client: *"No matter where I am right now and how bleak things seem, I did not get where I am because I was witless or inept. I did what I thought I had to do in order to get vital needs met. My previous coping style was effective given the limitations I had at the time. Now, I have **superior** life management skills and a greater understanding of how to meet my needs in a healthy way. I am on my way!"*

Client: *"No feeling, be it fear, anxiety or sadness is ever as unmanageable or devastating as I imagine in will be. Emotions, no matter how distressing or powerful, do **not** last forever."*

What concerns you most about changing?

Client: *"I'd suppose the intrinsic or viable, if you will, value of so great a 'turn around' at my age- 73! Like, suppose I could indeed change into a really comfortable, outgoing, spontaneous (occasionally zany) person. Where in the #!*@@ would a 73 year old, married 48 years, man go- Let alone - do? For now, I'm going to assume that I've just invented a **new** resistance behavior..."*

Can you pick out the resistances? It's too late, too much of a change. What will people think? I'm too old; I wouldn't know how to act. The way I am is comfortable. I am afraid to change.

What excuses are you using with your depression? *"I can't help it... I've been this way too long... No one can help me... I am afraid to take medication..."*

Resisting Change

SECONDARY GAIN THEMES:

1. **Getting attention** - This is a very, very difficult gain for depressed people to acknowledge. However, behavioral science tells us that all behaviors get attention. *"If I look and act depressed my family will _____ ...my friends will _____ ...co- workers will _____ ...my inner self will _____ ."*
    Client: *"If I feel bad enough I can justify some of my decisions."*

2. **Avoiding responsibility** - We gain this by using procrastination, anxiety, fear, illness and blame.
    Client: *"I can't be responsible for things right now because of my depression. My illness, anxiety, fear are because of how my family treats me."*

3. **Justifying dissatisfaction** - Looking for an excuse.
    Client: *"I can't go back to school, change jobs, improve my performance. I'm too depressed, sick and anxious."*

4. **Blame** - Self-pity, blame, and resentment keep us stuck; we allow it and therefore, are responsible for being stuck.
    Client: *"The company is in so darn much turmoil, no wonder I'm not doing well on the job. ... This is all my wife's fault. She's too demanding! She doesn't understand how bad I feel."*

5. **Avoidances -**
    a. avoiding the real problem
    b. avoiding doing things you dislike
    c. avoiding change
    d. avoiding getting truly close to people
    e. avoiding making decisions
       Client: *"It's all too complicated...if I am fully responsible for my life, my decisions...what if I make a mistake! I'd rather someone else make these decisions. I can be a "back ground" person."* If you sublet your life, you are not allowed to complain about how it's run!

6. **Fear of failure** - Review session three.

7. **What are your "problems" doing for you?** Make a list.
    Example: Smoking because I am defiant and defensive means I have a need to be defiant and defensive. Why? Where does this need come from? Is this still a valid need or is it a HABIT? (no pun intended).

Do you have questions, concerns or need support? Help is just a phone call away! Call-a-Coach 1-800-515-1133.

12-12

LESSON 12

Resisting Change

Action Assignments

1. The "basics." Renew your commitment to your daily use of the relaxation tape. This is also an important week to use your journal.

2. Review tape 4.

3. Pick three things you normally wouldn't try and try them.
   - eat something different.
   - wear something different.
   - do something you wouldn't normally do.

   Note your experience. From 1 (low) to 5 (high) rate your discomfort. What skills did you use to become more comfortable?

4. This week schedule two events you've been avoiding doing because of your anxiety and/or depression. Follow through using your new skills. (Breathing, positive dialogue, six steps to avoid panic) Note your experience in your journal. What positive insights did you gain about yourself?

5. Write a specific list of changes with deadlines and goals.

6. Be an observer of your inner motivations for your behaviors this week. Notice the "payoff."

7. Imagine yourself, do some visualizing, without this condition. Note what would be scary about your life.

8. Be kind, gentle and positive with yourself this week - this is one of the more difficult lessons.

9. Vigilantly watch for times when avoidances feel good. This will help you identify gains and resistances that are particular to you.

10. Look for the "mis-beliefs" that have kept you from changing.
    Client: *"If I stop smoking, the stress will give me cancer."*
    Is this belief realistic, factual or logical? Can I prove or support this with evidence? If I persist in holding on to this thought/belief, will I lead a happier life?

11. Be flexible. No decision, no change that you decide to make is "etched in stone." If you find that the way you are going about a specific change is not working, change **again**. You need the practice!

Final Comments

"....stop getting up at 6:05. Get up at 5:06. Walk a mile at dawn. Find a new way to drive to work. Switch chores with your spouse next Saturday. Buy a wok. Study wild flowers. Stay up alone all night. Read to the blind. Start counting brown-eyed blondes or blondes. Subscribe to an out-of-town paper. Canoe at midnight. Don't write to your congressman, take a whole scout troop to see him. Learn to speak Italian. Teach some kid that thing you do best. Listen to two hours of uninterrupted Mozart. Take up aerobic dancing. Leap out of that rut. Savor life. Remember, we only pass this way once."

Wall Street Journal, author unknown.

Sometimes it seems easier to stay where we are than to experience the anxiety of changing. We are creatures of habit; it may not be healthy but at least it feels familiar. The anxiety of living with these fears is much worse than the anxiety of changing and letting go of unhealthy beliefs and habits.

What could you accomplish if anxiety weren't holding you back? What if there were no more excuses? Isn't it time you found out?

Client: *"If the worst happens, I can control how anxious or depressed I feel. I am very creative. I can use the good life management skills I am learning and live a productive, positive, even happy life - despite truly tragic situations."*

Do you have questions, concerns or need support? Help is just a phone call away! Call-a-Coach 1-800-515-1133.

12-14

Lucinda's Letter

from *LESS STRESS PRESS*

Hello Everyone,

As some of you know, we moved to southern California a few years ago to pursue our career goals. We have experienced everything, including the earthquakes. Just recently, we experienced another disaster...the fires. Our house was less than a mile from being burned to the ground. We sat on the roof and watched the flames with hose in hand.

So, what does this have to do with enjoying the season? When you sit and watch devastation, and you see how quickly everything can change, you really put things into perspective. You realize how unimportant "things" are. You appreciate simply being healthy and safe.

As another year of hard work, unrealized expectations and unappreciated efforts cruises by, (I know many of you relate), I stop and think about how lucky I am. Sure, many things didn't happen that I would have liked to have happened, but look at all we have accomplished and all of the people we have helped! Look at the wonderful experiences I personally have had. I have a great family, a fun job and life is good. It isn't perfect, it isn't always easy...but it beats the alternative!

Living a good life no matter who you are, where you live, how old you are or what your circumstances are, has everything to do with daily decisions you make. You need to get up in the morning with the decision to:

- ✪ make it a good day
- ✪ stay calm and in control of your emotions
- ✪ say positive things to yourself and other people
- ✪ take time out to be alone with your thoughts
- ✪ pace yourself and slow down
- ✪ enjoy any little special moment that happens
- ✪ get outside and smell the fresh air
- ✪ pray gratefully
- ✪ exercise
- ✪ drink lots of water
- ✪ talk and laugh with someone who makes you feel good
- ✪ take one day at a time

I used to think..."*things will get better, slow down, be less stressful, etc.,when this or that happens. Then I'll feel better, more secure - less pressured.*" It doesn't work that way. There is no better time than the present day to enjoy your life, and besides, those "things" that might happen, also might not.

The simple choices we make everyday to help ourselves control our physical and emotional well-being really work. They certainly work for me.

Lesson Notes

LESSON 13

Time Management

"You are your first management priority"

Time Management: 12-Steps Toward a Balanced Life

OBJECTIVES - Lesson 13

* To understand that we choose how our time is spent.

* To get comfortable with "self" time.

* To become a great planner.

* To become more comfortable asking for help.

* To understand that over-scheduling can be an avoidance.

* To learn how our body, mind and spirit communicates: *"Enough for today!"*

* To cultivate the habit of frequently reassessing our priorities.

* To become more efficient and less anxious.

People who suffer from anxiety and depression often deplete their energy supply by constantly over-reacting to things and by feeling nervous and anxious.

Eventually, this nervousness and anxiety may make you feel exhausted, fatigued and depressed. Your adrenaline is working overtime.

People with anxiety disorders usually push themselves to the limit.

You are probably always racing against the clock with a thousand things to do in one day. You never stop and say, *"I'm tired. I've had enough. I'll finish tomorrow."*

It is very typical for people with anxiety disorders to plan too much in a day. As a result, by the end of the day you feel exhausted and unsatisfied with the day's accomplishments. This brings on panicky feelings. Your defenses are down. You feel dissatisfied with yourself. Your body is tired. It's the perfect setup for a panic attack.

You must learn when to say, *"I have had enough,"* and give yourself a break. This is a very important part of getting over this condition.

It is learning to recognize your body signals and letting them tell you when you are pushing yourself too hard.

It is learning to say "NO" to others who request too much of your time.

It is learning how to go through the day's activities and eliminate the ones that are not important.

Yes. It's possible.

It is learning to be more compassionate with yourself.

Most importantly, it is learning to appreciate and get comfortable with time spent simply relaxing and being with yourself.

Do you have questions, concerns or need support? Help is just a phone call away! Call-a-Coach 1-800-515-1133.

13-2

Performance Energy Test

How hard do you push yourself? Place a check in front of each statement that applies to you.

_____   I often do things for others even though I feel tired.

_____   I often take work home with me.

_____   I push myself to socialize when I don't feel like it.

_____   I often push myself to do things I don't want to do out of feelings of responsibility or guilt.

_____   I feel people take advantage of me.

_____   I often try to do two things at once.

_____   I find myself racing against the clock a lot.

_____   I often make stops or run errands after work.

_____   I often feel there isn't enough time in a day.

_____   I have a hard time relaxing. I feel guilty when I do nothing.

_____   I become irritated easily by the end of the day.

_____   I don't feel I have enough time to myself.

If you checked three or more statements, you have a problem managing your time. You are probably someone who isn't quite comfortable spending time with or on yourself. This is something you need to work on.

Give two examples of days or situations where you feel you pushed yourself too hard.

1. _____

_____

_____

_____

2. _____

_____

_____

_____

What could you have done differently to make it easier on yourself?

_____

_____

_____

_____

Is there an event coming up in the next few weeks that could cause you to have a rushed day? If so, what is the event?

_____

_____

_____

_____

Do you have questions, concerns or need support? Help is just a phone call away! Call-a-Coach 1-800-515-1133.

13-4

Guidelines

Here are some guidelines to follow to help you control the amount of energy you use in a day. If you only follow some of them, you will by amazed at how much better you feel by the end of the day. It will take a little practice because you are used to pushing yourself. You may even feel a little guilty at first. Show yourself compassion. You deserve to feel comfortable and enjoy your day.

- At the beginning of the day or the end of the previous day, take a look at what you need to do in that day. What can you eliminate? What really isn't that important?

- Is there something you could delegate to someone else?

- Break the day down into segments. Choose the most important errands or chores for the day and decide in what order you wish to do them. Don't start one until the other is completed, unless doing them together is more practical and convenient.

- Don't overload yourself for the day. It is better to underload yourself. Then, if you feel comfortable and have extra time and energy, you can add something else if you like.

- Take a break during the day to relax and think about something positive. Do something pleasant for yourself - even if it is just going for a snack in a pleasant atmosphere.

- Have a more relaxed attitude toward time. Nothing is that important in the overall scheme of things. Try not to feel pressured and rushed - especially when you are working, driving or running errands. Slow down and enjoy your time.

- When you feel tired, stop. Listen to your body signals. If you are starting to feel anxious it is because you are feeling pressured. Do what you can to relieve this pressured feeling.

- Avoid irritating, negative people if possible. If not possible, don't let them "get to you." Their problem is inside of them. Protect yourself by not reacting to them.

- Avoid caffeine and sugar.

- Plan to spend time alone at the end of the day to relax, read or listen to your tapes. Everyone can find a half-hour to themselves. If there is a will there is a way. Be assertive. You need this time.

Guidelines cont...

> ❧   Learn to say "NO" to other people's demands on your time. You will feel guilty at first, but eventually you will feel a wonderful sense of control.

> ❧   If you feel you are in a situation where you have to push yourself on a certain day, choose a way that will be the least demanding. Plan ahead. What can you do so the whole day comes off more relaxed? Have a more relaxed attitude as opposed to a rushed attitude.

Purpose and Spirituality

Living life on purpose, with **purpose**, is very important to your recovery. Anxiety and depression may continue after we have made changes if we haven't replaced old behaviors with new ones that give meaning and purpose. If you feel incomplete, like something is missing, ask yourself some questions: *"Where have I been? Where am I going? What am **I** all about? What in my life gives meaning to my existence? How are others better for my presence? What do I feel passionate about? What am I doing that feeds that passion? Am I fulfilled in my career, vocation and avocation?"*

People with anxiety disorders often feel trapped; this can be symbolic. Are you "trapped" in a job with no future, a relationship or situation that would require a huge risk to change? We can only encourage you to use the skills you've learned to overcome this avoidance behavior and gather the courage to walk toward changes that will lead you to greater meaning and purpose.

Take one day with the above questions; write about them. Plan on paper how you will go about beginning to live life with purpose. Maybe you will decide to see a career counselor, bounce what you are thinking off of a trusted friend. Maybe you will sit very quietly and listen for the answers that are within you.

We encourage you to nurture your spirituality. Acknowledging and seeking support from your spiritual beliefs is healing and leads to a basic faith and trust that we will "be all right," even when we make mistakes or confront something that we truly have no control over.

As a wonderful *beginning* we recommend:

- ▸   Chapter 14 in Lucinda's book, FROM PANIC TO POWER
- ▸   Volume II, tape 6, LIFE WITHOUT LIMITS
- ▸   SPIRITUAL WORKBOOK and DEVOTIONAL GUIDE, by Darla Van Horn, Jerry and Carole Wilkins. (See your newsletter for more information about these items.)

Do you have questions, concerns or need support? Help is just a phone call away! Call-a-Coach 1-800-515-1133.

13-6

Priorities

Please rank from 1 to 13 the priorities listed below that receive most of your time and attention. The priority that receives a 1 is where you spend most of your time; 13 receives the least of your time. Please feel free to add to the list. Be honest!

_____	Romance time with spouse/boyfriend/girlfriend
_____	Religion/faith/spiritual growth
_____	Money/career
_____	Health
_____	Entertainment/excitement/fun
_____	Intellectual or creative stimulation
_____	Friendships
_____	Your appearance
_____	Time with/on children
_____	Relaxation/peace of mind/"self" time
_____	Security
_____	Material possessions
_____	Clean/organize home

Now, using the above list of priorities, write out your priorities as you would *like* them to be. Where would you like to be spending your time? Obviously, the first priority on your list is your most important, with the last written priority being the least important.

_____	_____
_____	_____
_____	_____
_____	_____
_____	_____
_____	_____

What is interesting here is that most of us are spending an enormous amount of time on the wrong things! Often, you will find that when you are anxious or angry it is because your life is not balanced. Take a serious look at where you are spending your energy. Remember, it is up to you where you spend your time. What could you do to spend more time on those priorities that really matter to you?

Example Homework Responses to Lesson 13

Give two-examples of days or situations where you feel you pushed yourself too hard.

1. *"During preparation of an October budget submittal, I had to spend 2-3 days straight working on this project. I was forced to block out all other activity and work only on this project. I found it very stressful to block out all other requests for my time - saying "NO" to people."*

2. *"During a trip I made to Washington, D.C. and Scotland, I figured I had all this time during travel and in the hotels that I could get an enormous amount done. I took many things to do with me - more than I could accomplish. The unfinished things I brought along were on my mind constantly, which made it difficult for me to enjoy my free time."*

What could you have done differently to make it easier on yourself?

1. *"Be more compassionate and realistic with myself. I can't do everything. This was a high priority, short turn-around time project that needed to be done. I needn't feel guilty for dealing with priorities which are out of my control. There are times where I simply have to say "NO" to other people's requests for my time. Also, I could have had someone act as branch head to take care of the other concerns I had. Delegate."*

2. *"I should have taken only a few things to accomplish - along with some purely for personal enjoyment (like a novel). I would have been more at ease to do these few things and my time would have been much more satisfying."*

Is there an event coming up in the next few weeks that could cause you to have a rushed day? If so, what is the event?

My schedule for Tuesday: 11AM acupuncture, 2PM mammogram, 4PM doctors appointment. In between these three locations in the "big city" I also scheduled shopping. Because of what I learned in this lesson, I kept the three important appointments but did not try to shop. I arrived early for all my appointments and read a novel while I waited.

Do you have questions, concerns or need support? Help is just a phone call away! Call-a-Coach 1-800-515-1133.

13-8

Depression

When all is said and done, time can't be managed. It can't be pushed ahead, held back, shifted sideways or turned upside down. We can only manage ourselves and our choices.

Some important questions for us this week: Who is in charge of my time? Who is living this life I have? Whose life am I living?

When we allow others to manage and direct our lives, we slowly begin to feel empty inside. That's what depression feels like.

Time-Trials this week:

~ Call upon your network of supporters.
~ Think in terms of "Up-time" rather than "Down-time."
~ Break the day into half hour segments.
~ Under-load yourself.
~ Take breaks.
~ Have a more relaxed attitude toward time.
~ When you feel tired, stop! Rest **before** you need to.
~ Avoid irritating, negative people. (Write about this in your journal.) How did you feel this week? Better? Worse? The same?
~ Avoid caffeine, sugar and any other stimulants.
~ Schedule time alone at the end of the day. (How did you feel after the first time you did this? The sixth day?)
~ Say, "NO" to other people's demands of your time.
~ Plan ahead. Choose the least demanding plan.

Thought Question:

Are you choosing thoughts and situations that overwhelm and depress you?

Sometimes people unconsciously prefer helpless depression because it allows them to abdicate responsibility, therefore, they do not have to deal with their problems and make decisions. If you can relate to this idea, you may now see how one might gain something from anxious, sad thinking.

Action Assignments

1. Rededicate yourself to the basics of this recovery program: positive thought talk, relaxation tape and time, daily EXERCISE and no stimulants.

2. This week practice 3-D... Do it. Delegate it. Ditch it.

3. Brainstorm with people you trust and admire. Stop thinking of yourself as the "fix-it-person." The more minds you have researching a problem, the more ideas you will get. There is always more than one way to look at or fix a problem or concern. Watch out for pride and arrogance.

4. Write in your journal: Am I living an intentional life? Are you living on purpose, with a purpose? If you do not have time for your priorities, you will feel out of balance and depressed.

5. This week: DO NOT HURRY!

6. Use waiting time to practice patience.

7. Spend some time visiting someone in a nursing home. Some don't have the luxury of planning their time.

8. Make a list of all the things you do that are a waste of time and STOP doing them.

9. Spend fifteen minutes every day this week making a list of ways that you could be more organized. Write a plan that will enable you to accomplish this.

10. Review lesson seven.

11. PLAY!

12. PRAY!

Final Comments

It is often said of the anxious personality type, "It's not the big things that get us; it's the little stuff." Being organized, focused and clear minded about the use of your time is essential to a peaceful life. Stress, anxiety and depression creep in almost unnoticed the further we stray from being centered.

We all have twenty-four hours in our day. It is up to you what you do with them. Plan better. Delegate more. Relax and spend time alone. Slow down; you may live longer and you will certainly live happier.

Do you have questions, concerns or need support? Help is just a phone call away! Call-a-Coach 1-800-515-1133.

Accentuate the Positive

By Carolyn Dickman

from *LESS STRESS PRESS*

We have had two-letters regarding the statement, *"There is no safe place, no safe person."* Teri and Vincent were very concerned about this statement made by Lucinda on one of the tapes. Teri gave this enough thought to send a suggested revision of the statement: *"All places have the potential to be safe places."* Very positive thinking Teri!

Just to add our reassurances regarding this... because we are such negative, catastrophizing thinkers, some of us interpret that statement in a very black and white fashion. What Lucinda is saying is that **you** are your safe person - **you** are your safe place. **You** make the panicky feelings; **you** can turn them off (as taught in Lesson 2). No one can take the anxiety away, no place can take the anxiety away, **you** take it away by telling yourself that you can. **You** make you safe.

- **A Fact:** You decide how you feel.
- **A Fact:** You can't have a feeling without a thought first. (*"I can't handle this."* or *"I am in control. I am relaxing with each inhale and exhale."*)
- **A Fact:** Your brain has no choice but to believe what you tell it. (*"I'll be all right once I get home."* or *"I'm OK because I'm here."*)
- **A Fact:** The brain cannot distinguish between a real happening and an imagined happening. (*"What if an airplane lands right on the highway in front of my speeding car?"* or *"Stop! Breathe. What are the facts? What am I really nervous about - surely not an airplane."*)

If you believe in your mind that being in bed will make you safe, then you have decided that bed is safe. You may then experience feelings of safety while in bed. At one point in time, it didn't matter whether I was in my bed or in my car, I had panic attacks no matter where I was. When I lost my fear of the body symptoms, I no longer had them.

"You are your safe person and your safe place," is a positive thought. That means **I** am in control.

From the recommended book: <u>*The Portable Therapist*</u>, by Susanna McMahon... *"You can control your choice of how you feel about yourself; you choose whether you love yourself or you choose not to love yourself. Once you have chosen, then your behaviors...will follow your feeling. If you choose to love yourself, you will choose to behave lovingly toward yourself. You will accept and forgive and act more gently. If you choose not to love yourself, or not to make a choice (which is a choice in itself), then your behaviors will follow your training and you will ignore yourself, criticize and blame, externalize and expect perfection. It is within your control how you treat yourself. Because the world is treating you badly is not an excuse to treat yourself badly..."* (see newsletter for order form)

If You Have Complained About Being Treated Like a Doormat....*Stop Lying Down!*

Carolyn

Lesson Notes

"Is it worth dying for?"

-Robert Elliot

How to Keep Stress from Becoming Anxiety

OBJECTIVES - Lesson 14:

*   To understand that stress can create anxiety.

*   To understand that stress is an attitude.

*   To recognize environmental stressors and emotional stressors.

*   To learn to simplify your life.

*   To be able to use healthy reactions to stress.

*   To learn the power that comes from under-reacting.

*   To understand that stress is a message you give to yourself.

*   To understand that we always have choices: eliminate, modify or change attitude.

Stress is part of our daily lives.

Everyone is exposed to situations, events and people that are stressful.

Some stresses are caused by the environment. Some are caused by our emotional reaction to a particular situation. Some people choose to feel stress.

As we learned in Lesson 2, environmental stresses are things around you that cause you stress - marital problems, your job, children, illness, etc. These types of stresses are most often impossible to eliminate, but they can be minimized at times and they can be reacted to differently.

Emotional stresses are self-imposed stresses. They are stress responses to your own way of thinking. Not everyone has a problem with emotional stress. People who are very critical of themselves, who question their own self-worth, are the ones who suffer the most with emotional stress.

It is important to recognize what aspects of your life contribute to your personal excessive stress. Stress is an arousal reaction to an event, object or person. When you are under stress, you experience an arousal that is both physical, with body symptoms, and psychological.

Once you have recognized exactly what your stresses are, you try to eliminate some, minimize others, and change your reaction *response* to the stress you cannot change.

You can neither eliminate stress completely, nor would you want to. Stress can be a motivator. It can give you a form of energy that makes you feel like getting something done.

You can't always control the situation causing you stress, but you can control the way you react to it.

Do you have questions, concerns or need support? Help is just a phone call away! Call-a-Coach 1-800-515-1133.

14-2

Behavior Warning Signals of Problems with Stress

Check the statements below that apply to you. Check as many as apply.

☐   Feeling tired. Never really rested.

☐   Arguing with spouse, family members and co-workers over minor things.

☐   Lack of patience. Lack of tolerance of others' incompetence.

☐   Inability to feel relaxed.

☐   Constantly feeling under pressure because of job, personal life or finances.

☐   Feeling you don't have enough time for yourself.

☐   Feeling you don't have enough time for your family.

☐   Lack of desire or time to socialize.

☐   Absent-mindedness. Forgetting things.

☐   Feeling irritable and tired at the end of the work day.

If you checked two or more of the above, chances are good you are not handling stress in your life as well as you could.

Stress Test

Place a check in the left-hand column for each of those events that have happened to you during the last 12-months.

- ☐ Moving
- ☐ Death of someone close to you, miscarriage
- ☐ Divorce or separation
- ☐ Serious illness for you or a close family member
- ☐ Marriage
- ☐ Loss of job
- ☐ Retirement
- ☐ Pregnancy or birth of baby
- ☐ Career change
- ☐ Serious financial problem
- ☐ Children leaving home
- ☐ Problems among relatives
- ☐ Great personal accomplishment
- ☐ Increase in your or your spouses' work schedule
- ☐ Sleeping problems
- ☐ Serious problems with children
- ☐ Any major purchase such as a house or car
- ☐ Problems at work

If you checked three or fewer items and they fall below the top four in the list, you are experiencing an average amount of life's stressful situations.

If you have checked five to eight items, you are experiencing more than the average amount of life's stressful events. You need to view some of these stresses differently so you are not so upset by them.

If you checked more than eight items, you are over-stressed. You must do something to minimize other stresses in your life and spend some personal time each day relaxing and talking with yourself in a positive, compassionate manner. It will pass.

If you checked any of the top four items in the list, you are probably experiencing much distress. These are very high stress problems. You must give yourself permission to relax when possible as well as give yourself permission to feel somewhat anxious and distraught for a period of time. Do what you can at this time to eliminate other stresses from your life. It is most important to be compassionate with yourself now.

Do you have questions, concerns or need support? Help is just a phone call away! Call-a-Coach 1-800-515-1133.

14-4

What situations are causing stress in your life?

_____

_____

_____

_____

_____

How are you reacting to these situations?

_____

_____

_____

_____

How could you change the situation to reduce the stress? If you can't change the situation, how could you change your "reaction" to it?

_____

_____

_____

_____

_____

Name _____

List below any negative thoughts or statements you've had this past week. After you have written the negative statement, replace it with a positive statement on the next line. A space is provided below for the instructor to provide you with an example of a positive statement.

Neg. _____
Pos. _____
Ins. _____

Neg. _____
Pos. _____
Ins. _____

Neg. _____
Pos. _____
Ins. _____

Neg. _____
Pos. _____
Ins. _____

Neg. _____
Pos. _____
Ins. _____

Neg. _____
Pos. _____
Ins. _____

Neg. _____
Pos. _____
Ins. _____

Neg. _____
Pos. _____
Ins. _____

Neg. _____
Pos. _____
Ins. _____

Do you have questions, concerns or need support? Help is just a phone call away! Call-a-Coach 1-800-515-1133.

14-6

Homework -

We see so many different people in our groups, from all walks of life. They so often want to blame their stress and anxiety on someone or something around them. As you can see from this homework session, very often you cannot control your environment. However, you can always control your reaction to your environment.

This is the key. We all have stressful lives. You could be Chief Executive Officer of a major corporation, the mother of three children who has a full time job, or an unemployed male with too much time on your hands. If you are alive, you are experiencing stress.

Stress can have a positive effect. Stress, like anxiety, sets off a series of chemical reactions that can actually give you positive energy. Take advantage of this energy. Do something!

If you scored high on the **Behavior Warning Signals** assessment, you need to take action to eliminate as much stress from your life as you possibly can. (Good luck. Go back to your priorities.) Then you need to take action to view things in a less stressful way. Talk more slowly. Walk and drive more slowly. The fun is not the end result, the fun should be in getting there. Enjoy the getting there or you will be disappointed in the end result.

If you scored high on the **Stress Test** then you have obviously been through many difficult circumstances. This simply means it is time to baby yourself. Say "NO" to others demands on you. Put yourself first. Let others do things for you for a change. Pamper yourself. Most importantly, surround yourself with positive people and things.

What situations are currently causing stress in your life?

Most people write about situations involving other people. Remember, you can't control other people. Do you need to accept this issue, confront the issue or do you have the power to change the situation?

You always have the power to change your reaction to it!

Ask yourself, *"How could I under-react to this situation?"*

Depression

Stress that becomes chronic and/or excessive to the point that it begins to take a toll on your mind, body and spirit, frequently leads to some degree of depression. This fact can be a very exciting beginning for sufferers. If we resolve our problems (cause) with stress we change the effect.

Stress is often difficult to define because it is different things to different people. Two individuals could go through the same situation, one might define it as good stress, the other may feel it as **dis**-stress. **Your perception defines stress.**

Keep in mind:

1. Dis-stress triggers the fight or flight response which in turn releases several stimulants.

2. Your body responds to these stimulants in the same way whether it is a real situation or an imagined one from the past, present or future.

3. If you have had prolonged stress, you will find that you have mis-beliefs, negative attitudes and depressive thinking habits that perpetuate the cycle.

Observe your thought talk for twenty-four hours; keep a log. What are you talking yourself into?

You can stress yourself out lying in **bed**!

Research indicates that people who use humor as a coping skill suffer less depression, anger, nervousness and fatigue. Humor is a cognitive skill, developed by the user after repeated practice.

In this week's homework, you are asked to again review your thoughts and evaluate them. If you find some negative ones, write them down and rework them so that you have a nice paragraph of soothing, comforting, positive dialogue.

Any event or situation that you perceive as stressful can cause physical and emotional symptoms. The symptoms themselves are also perceived as stressful which adds more stress to an already stressful situation.

First aid: Whenever possible, down play or minimize the initial thought about the event or situation. Pay attention to your spirit, mind and body signals when stress is building, mange it before it begins to cycle.

Do you have questions, concerns or need support? Help is just a phone call away! Call-a-Coach 1-800-515-1133.

14-8

Action Steps:

1.   Stop - pay attention to the signals you have been receiving.

2.   Breathe - use 2-4 breathing for just one minute.

3.   Observe - Is my body tense? Where are my shoulders? How does my stomach feel? Listen in on your thoughts. How long have I been thinking negatively, a few minutes, an hour?

4.   Action - What is your plan for managing this stressor? Write it down, make a plan and work your plan.

5.   Learn - Take your experience with every episode of stress and learn from it.

LAPSE RELIEF:

Don't let a lapse throw you. Try to mentally rewind the last few days or weeks. When did you begin to notice negative thoughts and feelings? Begin to manage your breathing and thoughts. By interrupting unhappy thoughts we can short circuit sadness and not build on it.

1. Symptom manage (session 2 and 3 review)
2. Cognitive restructuring (session 3 and 4 review)
3. Gradual exposure to limitations and avoidances (session 8 and 15 review)
4. Practice coping techniques (session's 2, 3, 6, 7 and 14 review)
5. Maintenance work: relaxation tape, exercise, balanced lifestyle and kind cognitions.

Over the last few weeks you have already begun to manage stress, anxiety and depression more effectively:

> ~ you can now call upon the relaxation response
> ~ you are exercising and eating properly
> ~ you are avoiding stimulants
> ~ you are feeding your mind healthy dialogue
> ~ your expectations are becoming more realistic
> ~ you are getting a handle on anger and assertiveness
> ~ you have a plan for desensitizing
> ~ you are working on healthy attitude changes with regard to guilt and worry
> ~ you are doing the positive work that leads to healing from depression
> ~ and you are managing your time better

WOW! Look what you've started!

Action Assignments:

1.   Do the basics every day.

2.   Make a list of every stressor that you can remember from the last four weeks. If your spider plants aren't having babies and you've given this more than two minutes of thought time, list that also. Could you have avoided any of these? How many of them did you create? Which stressors were worth the time you gave them?

3.   List the positive changes you make this week as you manage your stress better.

4.   Ask two people in your life to remind you to Stop, Breathe 2-4, and Ask if this stressor is as important as my initial response. Construct a different plan of action.

5.   Practice your humor skills every day.

6.   Smile at least five times a day, at three different people.

7.   Spend at least 10 minutes picking out a humorous card for a friend.

8.   Share something positive with your significant other or a good friend(s) each day.

9.   Make a date with friends to go to a comedy club or funny movie.

10.   This week look for and write down three of the small things you find still cause stress for you. (These are usually things you are still over-reacting to. Practice under-reacting.)

11.   Don't miss the benefits of exercise as a stress reliever. According to research, stress reduction can last two to four hours after aerobic activity. Maybe we **can** run away from our troubles?

12.   Hang out with positive, optimistic and humorous people this week.

13.   Pursuing a healthy lifestyle is an ongoing process. Order a self-improvement book that the Midwest Center recommends.

14.   At the end of each day this week review your day: What new or good thing happened to you today? Did you see the sun rise? Set? Did you smell the particular season you are in? Did you receive a compliment today? Did you give a compliment today?

Do you have questions, concerns or need support? Help is just a phone call away! Call-a-Coach 1-800-515-1133.

14-10

Final Comments

Pay attention to your spirit, mind and body signals. The only means these parts of the whole can communicate with you is by causing discomfort. **Pay attention**.

It is **normal** to have body symptoms when anxiety and depression are present. Your body is functioning perfectly. Side effects are communiqués: *"Please change what you are doing."*

Feeling overwhelmed and stressed are a matter of choice. It begins with thoughts. Remember to keep it simple. Don't let your thoughts get the best of you. Stay peaceful. Stress doesn't have to turn into anxiety. It's your choice.

"BE" ATTITUDES

By Carolyn Dickman   from *LESS STRESS PRESS*

Someone once said: "*you will be the same person five years from now with the exception of: the books you read, the people you meet, the places you go and the risks you take.*" I would like to suggest that for the summer, you place that sentence in a conspicuous location-so that you can look at it often. What a great outline for your summer "95" journey!

I'm sure that some of you are familiar with beatitudes: "*blessed are the meek, for they shall inherit the earth, blessed are the sorrowing for they shall be comforted....*" (Did you know, the dictionary defines meek as calm?) I would like to share with you my "be" attitudes:

Be an avid reader. What a world this opens to us. After going through high school and college I, like most young people, thought I knew everything! (Bumper sticker I recently saw-- **"Ignorance should be painful."**) The more I read the more I know - I don't know. By the time I was twenty, my anxiety disorders were becoming very debilitating. One of my solaces was reading. Not only was I constantly looking for the answers to my problems, but I was also looking for moments of escape - reading was one of them.

I have bookshelves in the basement, in the laundry room, in the living room, in my office both home and in Oak Harbor, in my bedroom and kitchen. I love books. My dad once said, "*they can take away your money. They can take away your house. They can even take your life, but they can never take away what you put into your mind.*" I love and respect books so much that it was only within the last two years that I have allowed myself to write in them, to underline and hi-light. I have a very difficult time lending one of my books. (You know they never seem to come back.) If someone cataloged my books, I am sure that my life journey would be mapped. How can you give your life history away?

I know that not everyone is as fond of reading as I am. But with today's technology, books-on-tape, there is no reason not to avail yourself of the knowledge and insights of others'. I am a bookworm, but I am also a tapeworm! The average America spends over 400 hours per year in a car; make sure you have a reliable tape deck. We could go to graduate school in a Chevy.

I am nowhere near the end of my bibliotherapy. I have the great philosophers to read, more fiction, and endless self-help volumes yet untouched. I hope I have inspired you....you say you don't have time; you don't have time *not to*.

Be an interested observer of others. You will learn volumes. I have a sign above my computer: "*May I never be 'cured' of my curiosity!*" I love to listen and watch, whether it be at the mall or in the grocery store. Yes, sometimes it's painful. I often wonder how children survive the verbal abuse I hear--maybe some of them don't. At times it is so beautiful, a mother bends to her child's level and is actively listening to the "story" even though she obviously has much to do before dinner is ready.

Be a traveler. I know that some of you are working on this. Keep logging those miles; I promise it gets easier, and the rewards are countless. Some might say, "*easy for you, I have very*

Do you have questions, concerns or need support? Help is just a phone call away! Call-a-Coach 1-800-515-1133.

14-12

little money!" I have also always had very little money, but I have managed to make travel a part of my life, whether it was to a local museum, lake or potato chip factory. How many local points of interest have you checked out? Travel does not have to be expensive.

Having the incredible good fortune of working for the Midwest Center has given me many opportunities to travel. I have shared with some of you that I knew I was over agoraphobia when I found myself in New York City gridlock, on the Queens Borough Bridge (not in the outside lane), in a taxi with a very <u>strange</u> driver.

In every city I have been in, there was something very inexpensive to see and do. In California I fell asleep on a beach while listening to the Pacific Ocean. I got lost in a beautiful ranching valley. And I learned last year, that you can't feel after-shocks while driving in a subdivision, even though all the car alarms and burglar alarms are sounding. I've used second gear in my van while climbing a mountain in Pennsylvania. In Oklahoma, I caroused with a delightful couple on our program in a true country western bar. (I still can't do the two step - coordination was never one of my long suits.) I've visited many former presidents' museums, and had the most interesting of conversations in airport waiting areas. I once passed Robert Fulghum, author of "<u>All I Needed to Know I Learned in Kindergarten</u>." He looked so distinguished, with the most beautiful white hair, walking through an airport. I passed Heloise sitting outside a hotel. (I wonder what she thought when I said hello in full stage makeup, having just returned from a Hollywood studio.)

Yes, I have an advantage because of what I do for a living, but it didn't just <u>happen</u>. I made it happen; I said, "yes," even when I was so scared to do what I had said yes to that I could barely walk. You can do whatever you dare to dream to do if you say "yes" even when you are scared. Which brings me to my last "be" attitude.

<u>Be a risk taker.</u> No one knows the end of the story, your life story, but how it ends depends a great deal on your choices. *"Fear not, I am with you all the days of your life."*

Lesson Notes

CONGRATULATIONS! YOU'VE BEGUN!

Getting Beyond a Growth Spurt

OBJECTIVES - Lesson 15:

*   To completely understand that you hold the key to overcoming your anxiety and depression.

*   To be aware of the courage and tenacity that are present in the person who sets out to change life-long habits in thinking and behavior.

*   To be open to growth spurts. They are normal and merely represent an opportunity to polish your skills.

*   To understand that your goal is healthy self-management.

*   To see that this is only the beginning. You aren't done yet; you will never be "done" learning about YOU.

*   To see that: *"YOU are the LOCK, and YOU are the KEY."*

Congratulations! You are about to begin a more confident life with stronger, more effective coping skills. Some of you are doing extremely well. You may have a hard time believing you've come so far, so fast.

Others may be feeling that you are not as far along as you had hoped you'd be.

Remember, it takes 15-weeks to go through the program. Very often, it takes much longer to change behavior patterns.

Actually, you have only just begun to work on modifying your behavior. It may take another several months or so before you feel comfortable with the new behavior you have learned.

You will find yourself going for longer and longer periods of time without depression, anxious feelings or symptoms. That is when you will notice the change. You will find yourself handling certain anxiety producing situations differently, more effectively. You will think to yourself that you have grown. You will find yourself becoming more assertive. You will become more compassionate with yourself. All this will become more apparent as time passes.

Remember you are human. It is normal to have anxiety.

You will still experience anxiety, depression and nervousness at times. Everyone does. But, you will view it and handle it differently. It won't scare you the way it did before.

Do not strive for perfection when it comes to getting over your anxiety disorder. Perfectionism does not exist here. Give yourself permission to be human. Give yourself a break if you fall back into some of your old habits or if you have a panic attack. It is no big deal. This doesn't mean you are not better. It simply means your defenses are down for some reason. Recognize this and don't let it frighten you.

You will know you are doing well when you experience some of your old habits and fears and you give yourself permission to feel that way. Instead of getting carried away with, *"Why am I feeling this way?"* thoughts, you are saying, *"So what if I am feeling this way. It is normal and I am not going to let it scare me. One bad day or one panic attack is not going to ruin the rest of my week. I know what it is now. There is nothing to fear. I will be okay in a little while. I will feel better tomorrow."*

Do you have questions, concerns or need support? Help is just a phone call away! Call-a-Coach 1-800-515-1133.

15-2

This is where true recovery lies. Learning to be compassionate with yourself. Learning to give yourself permission to feel anxious sometimes and not let it scare you.

You are in control.

You may not quite believe that yet, but you will understand more and more as time passes and you begin to use your new skills. You choose to let things affect you. Choose to be less affected. Remember to talk to yourself in a soothing, comforting manner whenever you feel anxious and nervous.

We recommend that you go through the program again, at <u>least</u> once. Then feel free to pick different tapes at random to listen to.

You will be surprised at how much you might have missed the first time you listened to the tapes.

Each time you listen, you may pick up something new.

Basic Guideline's for Coping with Stress, Anxiety & Depression

- Recognize and admit that you are feeling stressed, anxious or depressed.

- Become aware of your body symptoms. Don't let them scare you. Let them talk to you.

- Try to pinpoint what it is you are anxious or depressed about. What happened yesterday? What were you thinking about before you went to bed? If you can't pinpoint it, don't worry about it and move on.

- If you do know what it is that is bothering you, what can you do to eliminate or minimize the situation in some way so that it isn't so stressful?

- Most importantly, how can you react differently so you won't be so affected by this situation?

- Listen to your dialogue to yourself. Are you filling yourself full of negative thoughts about a certain situation? What could you say to yourself that would feel more comforting and soothing?

- Are you filling yourself full of anticipatory anxiety before the situation even begins?

- Listen to the dialogue of those around you. Is someone around you being negative and dragging you down with them? If so, how could you change your reaction to their negative attitude so that you would be less affected by them?

- Are you overwhelming yourself with "shoulds" and high expectations? If so, which ones could you eliminate?

- Are you using anger at someone just as a means of venting your anxious feelings? Are you holding back anger that should be released?

- Watch your diet. Try to minimize the stimulants, especially when you are feeling anxious.

- Give yourself positive reinforcement for even the smallest accomplishments.

- Exercise at least three-times a week at your target heart rate. (220 minus your age, multiplied by .75)

Do you have questions, concerns or need support? Help is just a phone call away! Call-a-Coach 1-800-515-1133.

Growth Spurts

At this time, please complete the <u>ATTITUDE INVENTORY</u>© (below) that you completed back in your first week. Please see scoring directions from Lesson 1 (v-vi) to total your score. Complete the questionnaire and compute your score to measure your reaction to internal and external stressors.

As you read each statement consider it not on an intellectual level, but by your emotional and physical response when you make that statement. For example: Number 9, *"I must not fail!"* Intellectually you may know that we all "fail" and this is a part of life. But when you make the judgement that you failed, how does your stomach feel? Do you go over this "failure" again and again? For weeks, months, years? How does your head feel? What is your tension level? Reflecting in this manner, circle a one, two, three or four.

Step 1: Go through the statements at this time; circle the number that best describes your response.

1 = I never feel this way   3 = I frequently feel this way
2 = I occasionally feel this way   4 = I almost always feel this way

1. I like to be in control at all times 1   2   3   4
2. I like things to be fair 1   2   3   4
3. I have a hard time saying "no"
   without feeling guilty 1   2   3   4
4. I like things to be perfect 1   2   3   4
5. I have high expectations of myself 1   2   3   4
6. I worry about what other people think 1   2   3   4
7. If I want something done right, I feel
   I should do it myself 1   2   3   4
8. I feel guilty easily 1   2   3   4
9. I do not like to fail 1   2   3   4
10. I feel people should listen better 1   2   3   4
11. I don't like to cause conflict 1   2   3   4
12. People don't appreciate all that I do 1   2   3   4
13. I'm not where I want to be in life 1   2   3   4
14. There is not enough time in my day 1   2   3   4
15. I don't really feel rested 1   2   3   4
                                                           Subtotal   __ __ __ __

                                                   Total of all Subtotals   _____

Compare this score with your initial score. See how much you have improved! It does take time but with practice, you score will become lower and lower. You are a **great** student.

Depression

You may, because of previous conditioning, recall episodes of challenge: setbacks or relapses. We believe that the term "growth spurt," is not only positive, but it communicates the way challenging moments or days should be used--for growth.

Most humans, once they have made a change in behavior and attitude, experience lapses. [*"Lapse, a slight error...a temporary deviation..."* **Webster's New Collegiate Dictionary**]

Your "growth goal" is to see lapses realistically. They are single events, not catastrophes. Do not over-react. Remember what worked the last time, implement and learn.

Being aware of what makes us vulnerable to the "blues," we can be prepared and possibly divert it. Common high risk situations include:

1. Spending a few days in a negative emotional state, boredom, lowered self-worth, high stress or a number of small stressors.
2. Personal relationship conflicts.
3. Burn out and fatigue.
4. Focusing on the negative behavior of others and allowing this to influence us. We are still suggestible in the early stages of recovery - be vigilant.

You have the tools and skills (which include asking for help), to handle whatever comes your way. In essence- that is all we've ever needed.

Client: *"This program is like having a counselor on call twenty-four hours a day."*

You will always be sensitive. Now you know that this is not a curse, but a blessing. Stressors will come into your life, give yourself permission to feel normal stress and even a bit of the blues, when it's appropriate. The more you practice your problem solving skills and management techniques, the more you will handle them smoothly.

It is said that within each of us is a voice that knows what we need, knows what we should do. Listen and follow through.

Work hard on yourself- you are worth it. Take care of yourself in the ways that have always been missing. Balance!

Go out and claim your life....the life you were meant to live.

Do you have questions, concerns or need support? Help is just a phone call away! Call-a-Coach 1-800-515-1133.

15-6

Action Assignments

1. Continue to do the maintenance steps each day: exercise, relaxation, interrupt and replace negative thought talk and balanced living. Refer to your workbook often in the coming months.

2. Compare your final anxiety evaluation (15-10) with your first. Send to Midwest Center.

3. Do the depression evaluation again (15-12), compare to previous scoring.

4. Re-take the attitude evaluation from Session Four (15-5). Compare your scores.

5. High Risk Exercise: List five (or as many as you can identify) high risk situations that might lead to a lapse. Be very specific. Include names of people that may be involved, locations, behaviors, moods... For example: *"Becoming overly tired is a high risk for me."*

    Second step: Trace the history of the high risk situation. How have I experienced this before? For example: *"Based on my past history, if I allow myself to become over-tired, I find myself in a negative frame of mind. I over eat. I take on a victim attitude, "poor me." I see that over-tiredness always follows periods of high stress, over-work, and poor planning. I tend to commit to everything and everyone else. I do not put myself and my needs into the way I arrange my life."*

    Third step: Positive dialogue and Possible solution- *"I can see that being over-tired is a result of previous behavior and that is within my control. I can change this. I can prevent this risk situation. I know what I need to watch for."*

6. Consult your newsletter for recommended reading and extra tools. Seriously consider a subscription to the *LESS STRESS PRESS*. This will guarantee current information as the Midwest Center continues to grow and produce new self-help tools.

7. Read! Listen to motivational tapes.

8. Let time pass. Time allowance is necessary for proper growth. Patience is more than a virtue....it's a way of life.

9. If you think something you haven't completely dealt with is impeding your recovery, it probably is. Ask for the insight of an objective listener/therapist.

10. Continue learning about yourself. You are **fascinating**!

Final Comments

In this week's session, our goal is to put closure to the lessons and open the rest of the process. It is time to begin the rest of your life. From this moment forward - you are a problem solver.

It takes longer than a few weeks or months to change lifelong thinking behaviors. Plateaus are **normal**. It is also normal to occasionally fall back on old habits. Notice, learn and re-initiate healthy habits.

> ~ Give permission for stress or sadness when appropriate.
> ~ Be compassionate with yourself.
> ~ Recognize that you truly are in control of you.
> ~ Your inner dialogue will always be of primary importance.

Don't prejudge. You have been exposed to many new ideas and ways of "being." Sometimes, we just have to trust and "just do it," in order to know "it" is the right thing to do.

One or two uncomfortable days does not mean a major growth spurt is taking place. It's just a signal to investigate. It's probably a normal "down," everyone has "down" days. Don't over-react.

Live in the precious, present moment. The day of <u>absolute certainty</u> never comes - and that's all right.

Yes, there will be challenges, however that doesn't have to be scary anymore. You are sensitive, intelligent, creative and full of potential. The education you've put yourself in the way of over these last few weeks is IRREVERSIBLE.

> Client: *"...I have completed the program! It has changed my life. I'm not afraid anymore, I know I'm OK even when I don't think I am. I am more forgiving toward myself and others, I speak more gently. I feel more human and I have gained such a sense of achievement and confidence. But most of all, I believe in miracles. Because in my mind that's what this (evolvement and healing) is. I like who I am becoming."*

> *"...I am 23 years old, and at my young age, I have discovered what is <u>truly</u> important in life - family, friends, nature, exercise, relaxation, humor, smiling, being supportive, an ocean walk, a hug and kiss from my dog, a belief that any and all things are possible if you only believe it to be so...thanks a million."*

> Client: *"As long as we are anxious thinkers, we will have anxiety. When we change our minds, we change our lives."*

Do you have questions, concerns or need support? Help is just a phone call away! Call-a-Coach 1-800-515-1133.

15-8

Dreams can come true
if you take the time
to think about what you want in life...
Get to know yourself
Find out who you are
Choose your goals carefully
Be honest with yourself
Don't become preoccupied with yourself
Or think about yourself so much
That you analyze every word and action
Find many interests and pursue them
Find out what is important to you
Find out what you are good at
Don't be afraid to make mistakes
Work hard to achieve successes
When things are not going right
Don't give up
Find courage inside of yourself to remain strong
Give yourself freedom to try out new things
Don't be so set in your ways that you can't grow
Always act in an ethical way
Laugh and have a good time
Form relationships with people you respect
Treat others as you want them to treat you
Be honest with people
Accept the truth
Speak the truth
Open yourself up to love
Don't be afraid to love
Remain close to your family
Take part in the beauty of nature
Be appreciative of all that you have
Help those less fortunate than you
Try to make other lives happy
Work toward peace in the world
Create your own dreams
Live life to the fullest

    -Susan Polis Schutz-

ANXIETY EVALUATION FORM

Name _____ Today's date _____

Address _____

City _____ State _____ Zip Code _____

Phone _____ Age _____ Invoice # _____

Check the situations and events below that are uncomfortable for you due to your anxiety symptoms. **Using the two-scales below, indicate how often you would avoid the situation or event and how much anxiety you would normally feel in that situation.** If there are particular situations or events that bother you that are not listed, please feel free to add them at the bottom.

Level of avoidance scale	**Level of anxiety scale**
1 - never avoid	1 - minimum anxiety
2 - sometimes avoid	2 - moderate anxiety
3 - often avoid	3 - extreme anxiety
4 - always avoid	4 - panic feelings

EVENT	LEVEL OF AVOIDANCE	LEVEL OF ANXIETY
Shopping in stores	_____	_____
Eating in restaurants	_____	_____
Eating in front of people	_____	_____
Writing checks	_____	_____
Driving	_____	_____
Traveling distances	_____	_____
Standing in lines	_____	_____
Heights	_____	_____
Bridges	_____	_____
Sitting in meetings	_____	_____
Enclosed areas	_____	_____
Going to church	_____	_____
Socializing with people	_____	_____
Flying	_____	_____
Talking in front of others	_____	_____
Crowded areas	_____	_____
Being alone	_____	_____
Other	_____	_____

Anxiety Evaluation

Check below any of the body symptoms you experience during an anxious period.

○ racing heart/chest discomfort
○ trembling/nervousness
○ dizziness
○ feeling confused and bewildered
○ diarrhea
○ shortness of breath
○ numbness in various parts of the body
○ feelings of fatigue and depression
○ unexplained panicky feelings

○ nausea
○ hot or cold flashes
○ muscle tension
○ headaches
○ insomnia/sleeping too much
○ restless feelings
○ strange thoughts
○ feelings of helplessness
○ uncontrollable bouts of anger

How much do these symptoms bother you? Circle the appropriate answer.

Not much   Moderately   Extremely

Approximately how many times per week do you have panic attacks? _____

List the events, situations and/or opportunities that you have avoided this month in order to block anxiety, panic or feelings of depression:

During a typical day, how much time would you estimate that you spend worrying about this problem? _____

Are you on any medication for anxiety or depression? _____
What kind? _____ **Dosage?** _____

Have you seen a doctor for this problem? _____
Who? _____ **How long ago?** _____

What bothers you most about this condition? _____

_____

_____

How much does this condition disrupt your life? Circle the appropriate answer.

Not much   Moderately   Extremely

Where did you hear about The Midwest Center? _____

Additional comments about your problem you care to share: _____

_____

_____

_____

_____

Depression Assessment Scale

Name _____   Date _____

Within this assessment tool are 16-groups of statements. In each group, you are to choose the statement that most accurately describes your present way of thinking or feeling. Read ALL of the statements in a question before making your choice. Please circle only one number per group.

A. 1. I have had no unusual change in appetite.
    2. I have had a mild change in appetite.
    3. I have had a moderate change in appetite.
    4. I have had a severe change in appetite.

B. 1. I am satisfied with my weight.
    2. I am concerned about my weight.
    3. I am not satisfied with my weight.

C. 1. I have had no unusual change in sleep patterns.
    2. I have had a mild change in sleep patterns.
    3. I have had a moderate change in sleep patterns.
    4. I have had a severe change in sleep patterns.

D. 1. I am satisfied with the quality of sleep.
    2. I am concerned about the quality of sleep.
    3. I am not satisfied with the quality of sleep.

E. 1. I have had no unusual change in energy.
    2. I have had a mild change in energy.
    3. I have had a moderate change in energy.
    4. I have had a severe change in energy.

F. 1. I am satisfied with my energy level.
    2. I am concerned about my energy level.
    3. I am not satisfied with my energy level.

G. 1. I have had no unusual change in sexual desire.
    2. I have had a mild change in sexual desire.
    3. I have had a moderate change in sexual desire.
    4. I have had a severe change in sexual desire.

Depression Assessment Scale

H.   1. I am satisfied with my sexual desire.
    2. I am concerned about my sexual desire.
    3. I am not satisfied with my sexual desire.

I.   1. I have had no unusual change in self-perception.
    2. I have had a mild change in self-perception.
    3. I have had a moderate change in self-perception.
    4. I have had a severe change in self-perception.

J.   1. I am satisfied with my self-perception.
    2. I am concerned with my self-perception.
    3. I am not satisfied with my self-perception.

K.   1. I have had no unusual change in my ability to concentrate.
    2. I have had a mild change in my ability to concentrate.
    3. I have had a moderate change in my ability to concentrate.
    4. I have had a severe change in my ability to concentrate.

L.   1. I am satisfied with my ability to concentrate.
    2. I am concerned with my ability to concentrate.
    3. I am not satisfied with my ability to concentrate.

M.   1. I have had no unusual recurrent thoughts of death or suicide.
    2. I have had a mild amount of thoughts of death or suicide.
    3. I have had a moderate amount of thoughts of death or suicide.
    4. I have had a severe amount of thoughts of death or suicide.

N.   1. I am satisfied with the quality of my life.
    2. I am concerned with the quality of my life.
    3. I am not satisfied with the quality of my life.

O.   1. I have had no unusual change in my health.
    2. I have had a mild change in my health.
    3. I have had a moderate change in my health.
    4. I have had no unusual change in my health.

P.   1. I am satisfied with my health.
    2. I am concerned about my health.
    3. I am not satisfied with my health.

Depression Assessment Scale

Scoring

Questions A, C, E, G, I, K, M, and O demonstrate either physical or psychological symptoms. Add your score for those questions

> 8   absence of depression
> 9-16   mild degree of depression
> 17-24   moderate degree of depression
> 25-32   severe degree of depression

Questions B, D, F, H, J, L, N and P indicate personal satisfaction.

> 8   optimal personal satisfaction
> 9-16   concern about personal satisfaction
> 17-24   lacking in personal satisfaction

DO NOT let your score frighten you. If you feel you scored rather high and this concerns you, please talk with your physician about depression. It is common for people suffering with acute anxiety to be depressed. However, if your score is high, you might feel better talking with your physician.

All healing takes time, however, if you feel you are progressing too slowly, speak with your family doctor.

Welcome to the latest diet craze. On this diet you eat all the time, the servings are limitless. Wow! A dieter's dream come true.

WARNING This diet is not for your hips, it's it's for you mind and soul. You will lose all the negative, fearful, guilt-ridden, worrisome pounds that have kept you over-weight emotionally for too long. Shedding those pounds will be just as exciting and relieving as shedding physical pounds.

The results are even more rewarding and these changes will give you a whole new outlook and feeling about yourself. You must stick with it diligently. Cheating and feeding yourself the wrong foods, will result in gaining the weight back.

Too many negative carbohydrates, like fear, worry, guilt, self-doubt, anxiety and insecurity, stick to it and shed those pounds. **BON APPETIT!**

Michelle Jankowski ©

POSITIVE MENTAL DIET

Breakfast
1 cup self-love and self-respect orange juice
2 large bowls of frosted positive thoughts flakes
4 slices of self-encouragement toast, smothered with self-reliance jelly
6 strips of I have a choice, so I can and I will bacon
2 I deserve good feelings and things large eggs sunny side up

Lunch

2 big bowls of self-approval and self-assurance soup
2 large self-praise sub sandwiches with the works add heapings of self-acceptance sauce
2 large bags of confidence and belief in yourself chips
2 gigantic it's-OK-to-make-a-mistake-milk-shakes add 3 scoops of non-judging ice-cream

In-Between Meal Snacks

Treat yourself to handfuls of forget-your-negative-past-live-in-your-new-positive-present-with-love-patience-and-compassion-for self-and-others mixed nuts

Dinner
Appetizers, 3 combination platters of past and present accomplishment french fries, onion rings and take actions to face your fears fried mushrooms, topped with self-rewarding sauce.

Main Course
2 very large bowls of fun, laughter and play tossed salads pour on lots of fearless, worryless, freeing yourself from negative habits and patterns salad dressing
2 large look-at-what-I-can-do lamb chops seasoned heavily with inner-strength
2 heapings of relaxation and happiness vegetables
1 pitcher of no more doing it all, struggling for perfection and fear of failing ice tea. Add 2 accepting my mistakes and short-comings, learn-grow-and-move-on lemons
2 tablespoons of refusal to dwell, self-blame and torture myself for disappointments and let-downs, past and present sugar

Dessert

2 promising to care for myself as I would any other human being slices of pie
2 pieces of rewarding myself the things I've earned and deserve chocolate cake.
3 accepting self-uniqueness, intelligence and differences banana splits
6 pack of permission to live life positively without fear, insecurity or approval from others cola
1 roll of acknowledging and loving the child within myself always mints

- Michelle Jankowski ©

THE NEW COACHING PROGRAM

Congratulations! You have purchased the number one program in the world for overcoming anxiety, panic and associated depression. Since 1983, the tools and techniques of The Midwest Center have been used by over 300,000 people worldwide. This powerful program has evolved over the last 15-years. It is the most comprehensive, up-to-date resource available. If you have followed the schedule listed on pg. vii of this workbook throughout your course work, you have a new understanding of yourself and your true potential. You have come to accept your *special* personality/self, maybe even appreciate your sensitivity, ability to create, visualize and analyze. You understand the origin(s) of your condition. You are no longer a prisoner to victim thinking.

ATTACKING ANXIETY & DEPRESSION has taught you that it is your own thoughts, beliefs and inner dialog that is responsible for a large part of your distress. You no longer scare yourself with thoughts and images of doom and gloom. You have begun to look for the silver lining in every dark cloud; stay focused on the positive and the cards will forever be stacked in your favor. You have discovered a wealth of personal potential and desire that has been locked-up or forgotten in the recesses of your mind. *ATTACKING ANXIETY & DEPRESSION* has helped you develop a healthy, positive frame that works for you, not against you. I remain committed to providing you with the most cost and time efficient cognitive-behavioral based solutions - solutions that foster strength, character and self-empowerment.

With Commitment Comes Responsibility

With any commitment comes a certain amount of personal responsibility. It is not enough for me to just put the right tools in the hands of the people who need it most. I need to feel confident and secure in the knowledge that *each person* is receiving the <u>level</u> of help he or she needs. That is why we always suggest sending in your homework lessons and writing us those letters, **I need to know you are progressing**, if the program could be better or easier to use. Your comments and suggestions are more valuable to me than a whole panel of "consultant specialists." Like me, you have been there, WE KNOW WHAT WORKS FOR US! I also understand everyone is different. We all have vastly different life experiences, histories and dreams.

And that is why I invest in outreach survey campaigns, to record impressions and feedback about *ATTACKING ANXIETY & DEPRESSION*. This is how we learned there was a *need* for phone support services, amendments to the relaxation session, the Coaching Video series and the *LIFE WITHOUT LIMITS* follow-up program. In this regard, a consistent theme we have heard includes a strong desire for more *personal* communication between Midwest Center staff and program participants. While the comprehensive, self-help structure of the program is very effective on its own, a few participants have expressed a strong desire for more. These people wanted their very own personal advocate, someone to address their personal questions and concerns weekly. They request an informed, supportive ally who would motivate and guide them on their journey through recovery. I believe we have come up with a solution that accommodates this request without compromising our commitment to individual empowerment - an *Assisted Self-Help* model of care (**ASH**™): The Midwest Center Coaching Program.

ANNOUNCING: THE ATTACKING ANXIETY COACHING PROGRAM

ATTACKING ANXIETY & DEPRESSION is full of vital coping strategies, techniques and cognitive restructuring, but it is dependent on YOU and your effort, it can do nothing by itself. I believe that your own desire and personal strength will deliver you to where you want to be. However, some people have individual issues, concerns or weaknesses that keep them from where they really want to be in life. As individuals, we need to improve on our weaknesses and liabilities, only *then* can we progress and advance to that desired higher place. But that is the kicker, **human beings don't like to work on their own weaknesses**; it's uncomfortable, unpleasant and often overwhelming. That is why athletes need coaches, to support and PUSH them beyond their imagined limitations and boundaries. Athletes rely on the expertise and training of people who have been there before, people who are informed, cognizant, specialists in their field.

That's what the **_ATTACKING ANXIETY_ Coaching Program** is all about, having your very own personal coach to work with you through each lesson, *week by week*. Your coach will get to know you on a personal basis, he or she will be your ally, mentor and friend. Your coach will continually motivate you to challenge your status quo and help you explore the infinite options available to you. Working together, you and your coach will develop a customized plan of action, an inventory of your goals and the limitations you want to overcome. He or she will help you through these most difficult limitations and supplement each weekly lesson with a wealth of personal support and invaluable counsel.

You will communicate with your coach, from home or work, over the telephone. Because much of your interaction with others takes place in these settings, it will be easier to make the changes and implement the *constructive habits and behaviors* necessary for your personal success.

REALIZE GENUINE, LASTING CHANGE

ATTACKING ANXIETY & DEPRESSION is the comprehensive, yet cost-effective solution for debilitating anxiety and stress disorders. **The Coaching Program was designed to accommodate those individuals who require a higher level of individual support**. Again, it is my sincere desire for everyone suffering from this disorder to achieve the same peace I have found. So, if you do not feel you have realized your full potential, if you still feel limited by your stress and anxiety, you now have an assisted self-help option open to you. If you would like more information about The Midwest Center Coaching Program, call Paul at 1-800-896-7755 EXT 397.

Sincerely,

Lucinda Bassett CEO,
The Midwest Center for Stress & Anxiety, Inc.

"WHAT'S NEXT FOR ME?"

I have been helping people suffering from debilitating panic attacks and severe anxiety for over 14-years now. I have encountered many who, while not experiencing severe panic attacks, did often feel unfulfilled or dissatisfied with their lives, feeling powerless to bring about the benefits of positive change. They are not achieving in life what they had envisioned or hoped for themselves and feel unable to set constructive goals and follow the path to realizing these goals. What is interesting is that these people are extremely talented and creative. They typically have tremendous potential and yet few of them ever experience or realize this potential because they worry or fear failure. In addition, many people who successfully complete *ATTACKING ANXIETY & DEPRESSION* often ask me, *"OK, my anxiety is under control. What's next for me in my new life?"* I have spent the last year and a half writing and creating a new program entitled, *LIFE WITHOUT LIMITS*! How To Transform Worry and Fear Into Positive Energy, Success, and Fulfillment.

THE PROGRAM OFFERS SOLUTIONS TO LIFE'S CHALLENGES

This wonderful program is full of solutions to life's challenges as well as proven techniques for effective risk taking, dream building and goal setting. First it will help you clarify where your fear comes from, then it will help you to eliminate the fears and insecurities that only keep you from living up to your full potential. I worked very hard to make this program easy to use, compelling to listen to and lots of fun. This exciting new program includes: **Eight audio cassette tapes** full of powerful techniques for overcoming challenging situations. These tapes will help you to: break through common roadblocks to success, overcome your limitations and take productive risks, and break through your stress cycle once and for all. **A Journal of Potential** including take action steps for practicing what you have learned and recording your changing attitudes. **A 911 Feel Better Fast** tape to help you deal confidently with any challenging situation. This fabulous tape will help you analyze any stressful situation and come away feeling peaceful, confident and in control. And **A Weekly Desk Calendar** which is full of Positive Affirmations and inspirational quotations to help get each day off to a great start.

LEARN TO TRANSFORM WORRY INTO POSITIVE ENERGY, SUCCESS AND FULFILLMENT

This program is about the transformation of negative energy into a powerful positive force that will give you more confidence, more self-esteem, better communication skills, and unbelievable goal setting and risk taking abilities. *LIFE WITHOUT LIMITS* will give you a new appreciation for your life and your worth as a person. Learn and master the skill of empowering thought replacement, learn how to refine and create a success attitude within yourself and others, and turn procrastination and your fear of failure into confidence, excitement and success.

You can purchase *LIFE WITHOUT LIMITS* for only $159.96 plus shipping or four easy payments of $39.99 plus shipping. This program will show you how to tap into the universal energy that is available to all of us, and that I have utilized many times to bring things into my life. You can learn how to re-channel your energy and make it work for you instead of against you. I hope you give this new program a try, the feedback I have received is so exciting! I think you will be very pleased with your results.

SATISFACTION GUARANTEED, OF COURSE!

LIFE WITHOUT LIMITS comes with a 30 day money back guarantee, so once purchased you have a month to preview *LIFE WITHOUT LIMITS* on a trial basis. If you are dissatisfied, simply return the program in new condition for a full refund less shipping and handling. I wish you a life that meets your greatest expectations!

Fondly,

Lucinda Bassett

"I purchased ATTACKING ANXIETY over 5 years ago and have recently purchased Lucinda's new program LIFE WITHOUT LIMITS, and by golly, it seems that she's going to change my life again!"
Cindy T. 42 Philadelphia, Pa.

"I've been struggling ever since my father past away recently. These tapes made me feel like I had a best friend and really helped me out of my depression. I am very happy with the entire program!"
Lisa M. 33 Dallas, Tx.

"The most valuable lesson I've learned from LIFE WITHOUT LIMITS is to be more assertive, to not take no for an answer when a issue is important to me. I have a much more positive outlook on life."
Richard W. 58 Madison, Wi.

"I never realized how your point of view could determine your attitude and your general overall happiness. I'm a much better person thanks to this program." **Nancy B. 28 St. Paul, MN.**

tear off and include with payment

You can own *LIFE WITHOUT LIMITS* for $159.96 or four easy payments of $39.99.

For more information or for Credit Card orders call: **1-800-944-9428** or
Send to: **Midwest Center, 106 N. Church St. Suite 200, PO box 205, Oak Harbor, Oh 43449**

___ **1 Pay Plan $159.96***   ___ **4 Pay Plan of $39.99* per month**
            ***add $9.95 for S&H on first payment ONLY!**

_ **Visa/Mastercard**   _ **Discover**   _ **American Express**   _ **Money order**   _ **Check**

Card Number_____ **Expiration Date** _____

Signature of card holder_____

Name of person enrolling _____

Address _____

City _____ **State** ____ **Zip** _____ **Phone** _____

Lucinda's Letter

from *LESS STRESS PRESS*

Hello Everyone!

The theme of this particular newsletter issue is positive self-talk. What a perfect time to tell you about my new book, <u>*From Panic to Power*</u>, *Proven Techniques to Calm Your Anxieties, Conquer Your Fear, and Put You in Control of Your Life.* HarperCollins*Publishers.*

I am very proud of this book. So often, people ask me, "*What is your story. How did your anxiety affect your life? How did it affect your relationships and how did you recover?*" Well, it's all in this book. I am particularly proud of how I wrote <u>*From Panic to Power*</u>. I wrote it from the heart. Right about now, with the book being released and reviewed, it would be really easy to start "What-ifing." "*What if the reviews are bad? What if editors don't think it's 'intellectual' enough? What if doctors don't think it's clinical enough?*" Don't think I haven't had these thoughts. But that is when my positive self-talk takes over. This book is wonderful. It is motivating, warm, spiritual and very candid because I share so much of my personal life. And guess what? I didn't write this book for the critics, the editors or the doctors. I wrote it for people like us. I wrote it for people who want to hear from someone who has been where they are - someone who transformed their anxious, worrisome thoughts into something positive and fulfilling - someone who was so consumed with fear they couldn't function, and now they are so motivated about living life fully they can hardly sit still.

I wanted people to open this book and say, "*You mean I am special because of my anxiety? You mean I have tremendous potential because I am prone to anxiety?*" Yes, you are and you do. You simply need to re-direct all that creative energy so that it stops making you feel afraid and starts making you feel confident and capable of great things. It all begins with changing the way you think, the messages you give yourself.

It wasn't easy to write a great book. And I really believe it is a great book. I wasn't easy to get a book contract. I wasn't easy to create the **Attacking Anxiety & Depression** Program. But life, freedom, fulfillment and happiness aren't about things being easy. It's about effort and resilience. It's about staying focused and never quitting. The book focuses on how to be strong, how to go after your dreams and how to be a better decision maker and risk taker.
       Here are a few of the topics covered in the book:

- Where Do You Run When Panic Attacks?
- Taking Responsibility for the Way You Feel for the Rest of Your Life
- How to Jump Off the Edge and Be Your Own Parachute
- Leap of Faith: Free at Last!

- The Attitude of Achievement
- You Have to Be the One You Run To
- How to Stop Being Disappointed and Start Getting What You Want
- To Medicate or Not to Medicate: That is the Question

Here is the good news. I just received my first book review from *Publishers Weekly* and it was just wonderful! Also, *Cosmopolitan Magazine* wants to use segments of Chapter Seven in their January issue. You can bet I am going to keep using that positive self-talk!

There is so much in <u>*From Panic to Power*</u> that I want to share with you. I hope you will wander into your local bookstore and pick up a copy or two. You'll know me that much better and you'll know yourself a little better too.

Remember, you are capable of great things. Once you overcome your fears, anything is possible.

Until next time...   God Bless,   Lucinda

Workbook Index